# J. K. LASSER'S
# LEGAL AND
# CORPORATION FORMS
# FOR THE
# SMALLER BUSINESS

## ARNOLD GOLDSTEIN,
## EDITORIAL CONSULTANT

**MACMILLAN • USA**

Second Edition

Macmillan General Reference
A Prentice Hall Macmillan Company
15 Columbus Circle
New York, NY 10023

A J.K. Lasser™ Book

J.K. LASSER and the J.K. LASSER INSTITUTE are registered trademarks of Simon & Schuster, Inc.
MACMILLAN is a registered trademark of Macmillan, Inc.

ISBN 0-671-88327-5 (book-only version)
ISBN 0-671-88434-4 (book/software disk version)

Manufactured in the United States of America

10  9  8  7  6  5  4  3  2  1

This book is sold with the understanding that neither the author nor the publisher is engaged in rendering legal advice. If legal advice is required, the services of an attorney should be sought. Publisher and author cannot in any way guarantee that the forms in this book are being used for the purposes intended and, therefore, assume no responsibility for their proper and correct use.

# LIST OF FORMS

**Section 1**     **Organizing Your Business   L   1**

What Form Is Best For Your Business?   L   3
Sole Proprietorship   L   5
Partnership   L   6
Limited Liability Company (LLC)   L   8
Corporation   L   9
State and Local Requirements for Creating a Corporation   L   14
Where to Incorporate   L   16
Tax Aspects of Incorporation   L   26
The Certificate or Articles of Incorporation   L   28
Checklist   L   30


**Section 2**     **Resolutions on Corporate Structure and Governance   L   31**

Stockholders' Resolution (Name Change)   L   33
Directors' Resolution (Amend Articles)   L   34
Stockholders' Resolution (Amend Articles)   L   35
Certificate of Stockholders' Consent   L   36
Certificate of Amendment   L   37
Stockholders' Resolution (Amend By-Laws)   L   38
Certificate of Stockholders' Consent   L   39
Directors' Resolution (Amend By-Laws)   L   40
Stockholders' Resolution (Increase Stock)   L   41
Directors' Resolution (Dissolve Corporation)   L   42
Stockholders' Resolution (Dissolve Corporation)   L   43
Affidavit of Secretary   L   44
Certificate of Dissolution   L   45


**Section 3**     **Resolutions on Major Corporate Actions   L   47**

Directors' Resolution (Authorize Contract)   L   49
Directors' Resolution (Appoint Counsel)   L   50
Directors' Resolution (Commence Suit)   L   51
Stockholders' Resolution (General Borrowing)   L   52
Directors' Resolution (Authorization to Borrow)   L   53
Directors' Resolution (Sell Real Estate)   L   55
Directors' Resolution (Acquire Real Estate)   L   57
Directors' Resolution (To Lease)   L   59
Directors' Resolution (Proposed Contract)   L   60
Directors' Resolution (To Contract)   L   61
Certificate of Stockholders' Consent   L   62
Directors' Resolution (Agreement to Merge)   L   63


**Section 4**     **Resolutions on Compensation and Dividends   L   65**

Directors' Resolution (Employee Stock Option)   L   67
Directors' Resolution (Pay Honorarium)   L   68
Directors' Resolution (General Bonus)   L   69
Directors' Resolution (Expense Reimbursement)   L   70
Directors' Resolution (Issue Stock Dividend)   L   71
Directors' Resolution (Automatic Dividends)   L   72
Directors' Resolution (Pay Quarterly Dividends)   L   73
Directors' Resolution (Retain Earnings)   L   74
Directors' Resolution (Repayment of Disallowed Expenses)   L   75
Certificate of Consent (Repayment of Disallowed Expenses)   L   76

**Section 5**      **Resolutions on Employee Benefits   L 77**

Directors' Resolution (Profit-Sharing Plan)   L 79
Directors' Resolution (Pension Plan)   L 81
Directors' Resolution (Employee Stock Option)   L 82
Directors' Resolution (Medical Care Plan)   L 83
Directors' Resolution (Wage Continuation Plan)   L 84
Directors' Resolution (Group Legal Services)   L 85
Directors' Resolution (Group Insurance)   L 86
Directors' Resolution (Employee Benefit Plan)   L 87
Directors' Resolution (Employee Welfare Plan)   L 88
Directors' Resolution (Death Benefits)   L 89
Directors' Resolution (Loan to Officer)   L 90


**Section 6**      **Miscellaneous Corporate Documents   L 91**

Stock Transfer Ledger   L 93
Stock Certificate   L 95
Application for Employer I.D. Number   L 96
Election By a Small Business Corporation   L 97
Instructions For Form 2553 (S Corporation)   L 99
Assignment of Assets   L 101


**Section 7**      **Organizational Meetings and By-Laws   L 103**

Notice of Organization Meeting of Incorporators and Directors   L 105
Waiver of Notice of Organization Meeting of Incorporators and Directors   L 106
Minutes, First Meeting of Shareholders   L 107
Minutes of Organization Meeting of Board of Directors   L 109


**Section 8**      **Annual and Special Meetings   L 111**

Notice to Shareholders of Annual Meeting   L 113
Minutes, Shareholders' Annual Meeting   L 114
Notice to Directors of Regular Board Meeting   L 117
Minutes, Regular Board Meeting   L 118
Minutes of Directors' Meetings   L 120
Minutes of Special Meeting of Stockholders   L 122


**Section 9**      **Basic Agreements   L 125**

Agreement With Sales Representative   L 127
Confidentiality Agreement   L 129
Consignment Agreement   L 131
Partnership Agreement   L 132
Contractor Agreement   L 136
Contract for Sale of Personal Property   L 138
Arbitration Agreement   L 139
Covenant Not To Compete   L 140
Indemnity Agreement   L 141
Conditional Sale Agreement   L 143
Stock Subscription Agreement   L 145
Purchase Requirement Agreement   L 146
Open Listing Agreement   L 147
Agreement to Assume Debt   L 148
Extension of Agreement   L 149
Agreement to Extend Performance Date   L 150
Mutual Termination of Contract   L 151

## Section 10    Employment    L 153

Employment Agreement    L 155
Job Applicant Waiver Form    L 159
Employment Acknowledgement (Part-Time or Temporary)    L 160
Night Shift Agreement    L 161
Independent Contractor Acknowledgement    L 162
Conflict of Interest Declaration    L 163
Notice of Confidentiality Agreement    L 164
Employee Agreement Not to Disclose    L 165
Employee Agreement on Proprietary Rights    L 167
Employee Agreement on Inventions and Patents    L 169
Employee Warning Notice    L 172
Authorization to Release Employee Information    L 173
Employee Resignation    L 174

## Section 11    Loans and Borrowing    L 175

Consumer Loan Agreement    L 177
Promissory Note    L 179
Secured Promissory Note    L 180
General Guaranty    L 182
Guaranty Termination Acknowledged    L 184
Notice of Purchase Money Security Interest    L 185
Right of Rescission Notice    L 186
Discharge of Security Interest    L 188
Pledge of Property    L 189
Notice of Default on Promissory Note    L 191
Demand For Payment on Promissory Note    L 192
Demand For Payment on Guarantor    L 193
Demand For Payment on Endorsers    L 194
Demand by Secured Party For Repossession of Collateral    L 195
Surrender of Collateral    L 196
Notice of Public Sale of Collateral    L 197
Notice of Private Sale of Collateral    L 198
Notice to Subordinate Lienholder of Foreclosure and Intended Sale    L 199

## Section 12    Credit and Collections    L 201

Credit Information Request    L 203
Request For Bank Credit Reference    L 204
Request For Credit History    L 205
Credit Reference Acknowledgement    L 206
Credit History Transmittal    L 207
Partial Shipment Request    L 208
Notice of C.O.D. Terms    L 209
Agreement to Apply Trade Allowances    L 210
Notice of Unpaid Invoice    L 211
Discount Disallowed Notice    L 212
Payment Inquiry    L 213
Second Notice of Overdue Account    L 214
Demand For Payment    L 215
Final Collection Notice Prior to Legal Action    L 216
Request For Information on Disputed Charge    L 217
Settlement Offer on Disputed Account    L 218
Installment Payment Acknowledgement    L 219
Confirmation of Payment Plan    L 220
Notice of Default on Extension Agreement    L 221
Creditor's Affidavit    L 222
Turnover For Collection    L 223

Debt Acknowledgement   L 225
Assent and Proof of Claim   L 226
Debt ReAffirmation   L 227
Authorization to Release Credit Information   L 228
Adverse Credit Information Request   L 229

## Section 13   Buying/Selling Goods  L 231

Verbal Order Confirmation   L 233
Purchase Order Exceptions   L 234
Acknowledgement of Modification of Contract Terms   L 235
Demand For Acknowledgement of Shipping Dates   L 236
Demand For Delivery   L 237
Notice of Refusal to Accept Delivery   L 238
Notice of Rejection of Goods   L 239
Notice of Cancellation of Back-Ordered Goods   L 240
Notice to Cancel Order Due to Delayed Shipment   L 241
Notification of Non Conforming Goods   L 242
Notice to Seller of Defective Goods   L 243
Acceptance of Damaged Goods   L 244
Confirmation of Goods Received   L 245
Sale on Approval Acknowledgement   L 246
Notice of Withheld Delivery   L 247
Acceptance of Order With Delivery in Lots   L 248
Notice of Product Defect Claim   L 249
Notice of Resale   L 250
Notice to Stop Goods in Transit   L 251
Notice to Reclaim Goods   L 252
Authorization to Return Goods   L 253

## Section 14   Leases and Tenancies  L 255

Lease   L 257
Lease Extension Agreement   L 259
Agreement to Terminate Lease   L 260
Sublease Agreement   L 261
Lease Assignment   L 263
Notice to Exercise Lease Option   L 264
Landlord's Waiver to Tenant's Fixtures   L 265
Tenant's Notice Terminating Tenancy   L 266
Legal Vacate Notice   L 267

## Section 15   Transfers and Assignments  L 269

General Bill of Sale   L 271
Warranty Bill of Sale   L 272
Quitclaim Bill of Sale   L 273
Assignment of Accounts Receivable With Recourse   L 274
Assignment of Accounts Receivable With Non-Recourse   L 275
Copyright Assignment   L 276
Assignment of Income   L 277
Assignment of Trademark   L 278
Notice of Assignment   L 279
Bond and/or Stock Transfer   L 280

## Section 16    General Legal Forms   L 281

General Contract   L 283
Affidavit   L 284
General Power of Attorney   L 285
Revocation of Power of Attorney   L 287
Individual Acknowledgement   L 288
Corporate Acknowledgement   L 289
Receipt in Full   L 290
Receipt on Account   L 291
Sight Draft   L 292
Notice of Dishonored Check   L 293
Stop-Payment Order   L 294
Stop-Payment Order Cancellation   L 295
Bulk Sales Notice   L 296
Covenant Not to Sue   L 297
Release of Mechanics' Liens   L 298
Permission Request   L 299
Permission to Use Quote or Personal Statement   L 301
Purchase Option   L 302
Gift Acknowledgement   L 303
Name Removal Request   L 304
Notice of Disputed Account Balance   L 305
Payment on Specific Accounts   L 306

# ABOUT THIS BOOK

This book can help you in many different ways.

It has over 300 forms covering a wide range of transactions.

Whatever your business, you'll find legal agreements and forms to help you. Whether you are buying or selling goods or hiring or firing an employee, you must use the right legal documents.

With *J.K. Lasser's Legal and Corporation Forms for the Smaller Business*, you'll have virtually every corporate and legal form you and your business need to:

* Save hundreds of dollars a year in legal fees

* Increase profits by helping you to improve efficiency and performance in every phase of your business

* Avoid dangerous lawsuits and costly claims

* Cut corporate and personal taxes

* Provide an accurate record of major corporate events

* Streamline the often tedious chore of maintaining corporate records

# HOW TO USE THIS BOOK

The forms in this book can be easily completed and used. Just review the table of contents and you will find forms corresponding to the legal or corporate activity you are undertaking. There may be two or more forms for a particular purpose, so compare the several forms for the one most suitable to your needs. The forms can be easily modified, if required, by adding or deleting provisions.

1. Before completing each form, remove it from the book and have it photocopied so you can retain the originals for future use. Complete the copy and reproduce as many as necessary for other parties to the transaction, the corporate minutes book, or your own files. If you are using the version of this book that includes a software disk, you'll find complete user's instructions at the front of the book. Those instructions will tell you how to use the disk to add personalized information to your own versions.

2. Correspondence forms can also be reproduced on your own letterhead and photocopied in quantity for future use.

3. Some forms have specific footnoted instructions. The footnotes are there for your protection, so follow them carefully.

4. Important correspondence should always be delivered by certified mail, return receipts requested. Although not legally required for most legal correspondence, this will prove notice of receipt.

5. As with all business records, retain completed copies for at least six years, since most lawsuits and other legal actions must be commenced within this time period.

The forms in this book frequently use the pronoun "it" to refer to a given party. It is acceptable to use "it" in place of "him" or "her" when referring to a natural person, so no change is required. Also "it" is the appropriate pronoun to designate a corporation, partnership, or any other legal entity.

## A FINAL WORD ON USING STANDARD FORMS

No do-it-yourself book can take the place of an attorney or accountant when serious legal, accounting, or tax issues are involved. The forms in this book contain basic clauses that should be included in a legal document, but you should exercise caution. Documents in a forms book such as this are often starting points requiring modification to fit your individual requirements. Use common sense to decide when it's time to consult an attorney rather than rely on the forms in this or any other book.

You certainly need your attorney to draft complex or important agreements, and for transactions involving substantial amounts of money, or for any matter where you don't understand the proper use of a form or if you have any doubts about its adequacy to protect you on a particular transaction.

Remember—we cannot in any way guarantee that the forms in this book are being used for the purposes intended and, therefore, neither the publisher nor author can assume responsibility for their correct use; nor can they assume liability for their improper use.

Why not have your attorney review the forms in this book and help you decide which forms can be safely adopted for self-use within your business?

## THE FORM YOU NEED IS EASY TO FIND

To help you locate the right form, you'll find the forms in this book are grouped by section and cross-indexed alphabetically. It's easy to find just the form you need. But why not review all the forms in this book in advance? You'll discover many useful forms and the many ways in which *J.K. Lasser's Legal and Corporation Forms for the Smaller Business* can help you.

# Organizing Your Business

# WHAT FORM IS BEST
# FOR YOUR BUSINESS?

Whether to incorporate or to conduct a business in some other form—such as a

sole proprietorship or a partnership—involves many considerations. If you are currently

doing business, don't let work pressures prevent you from carefully considering whether

the current form of your enterprise is the best one for you. If you are not yet in business

but plan to start soon, first take the time to decide which type of structure is the right one

for your new venture. Many factors go into the considerations of the form and structure

of a business enterprise:

1. liability and personal exposure

2. costs, including filing fees

3. tax considerations

4. the available methods of raising capital

5. the ability to attract and keep key personnel through various fringe benefits

   or participations such as stock options

The three basic forms of business entity are:

1. individual or sole proprietorship

2. partnership

3. corporation

In states that allow it, you may also consider organizing a business as a limited

liability company (LLC), which combines certain features of partnerships and

corporations.

Each form of business organization offers advantages and disadvantages.

If you are going into business without partners, your choice is between operating

as a sole proprietor or incorporating. If you have partners, your choice is among a partnership, corporation, or limited liability corporation. For tax purposes, a corporation

may be set up either as a regular corporation or as an S corporation.

In discussing with your attorney and accountant which business form to use,

consider not only your immediate business plans and personal financial and tax

concerns, but also your future objectives.

# SOLE PROPRIETORSHIP

A sole proprietorship is a business that is owned by an individual who is solely responsible for all aspects of the business. The owner is personally responsible for all debts of the business even in excess of the amount invested.

As a self-employed sole proprietor, you report business income and expenses on your personal tax return.

*The advantages of a sole proprietorship include:*

1. Low start-up costs since legal and filing fees are at a minimum. However, many states and cities require at least a filing with the county clerk, especially if a fictitious business name is adopted. Obtaining local licenses may also be necessary.

2. Greatest freedom from regulation.

3. Owner is in direct control.

4. Minimum working capital requirements.

5. Tax advantages to individual owners of small businesses may be available.

6. All profits inure to the owner.

*The disadvantages include:*

1. Unlimited liability. The proprietor is responsible for the full amount of business debts no matter how incurred, which means that his or her personal property may be taken to cover debts of the business.

2. Unstable business life, since the sole owner's death or illness effectively terminates the business.

3. Difficulty in raising capital and in obtaining long-term financing.

# PARTNERSHIP

A partnership is a legal entity that is jointly owned by two or more individuals (although in some cases partners may also be corporations or other entities). As in the sole proprietorship, the owners are personally liable for all debts of the firm unless a special type of partnership, the limited partnership, is set up. Limited partnerships are very complex legal structures in which at least one general partner must have unlimited liability. Partnership agreements can be quite complex.

For tax purposes, the partnership must report income and expenses to the IRS, but the partnership itself does not pay taxes. Each partner reports his or her share of the partnership income or losses on his or her individual tax return.

*The advantages of a partnership include:*

1. Ease of formation (although more complicated than the sole proprietorship).

2. Low start-up costs, especially since there usually are fewer filing fees and franchise taxes than for a corporation.

3. Limited outside regulation, unless the type of business itself is one that is in a regulated industry.

4. Broader management base than in a sole proprietorship yet a more flexible management structure than that of the corporation.

5. Direct rewards of the profits of a business.

6. Possible tax advantages, since a partnership avoids the double taxation of corporations and because income can be taxed at personal income rates. However, the personal income situations of the partners could also make this a disadvantage.

7. Additional sources of capital and leverage by adding limited and special partners.

8. Each partner can bind all of the co-partners, and, in the absence of restrictions in the partnership agreement, can terminate the partnership.

9. The duration of the entity can be limited to a stated time or can continue indefinitely by amendment.

*The disadvantages of a partnership include:*

1. Except in limited partnership situations, all the partners have unlimited liability. The personal assets of the general partners are available to satisfy partnership debts.

2. The life of a partnership is unstable since changing partners by adding new ones or by death or departure of partners may cause the partnership to terminate unless a clause in the partnership agreement provides otherwise.

3. Obtaining large sums of capital is relatively difficult as the financing cannot be obtained from the public through a stock offering.

4. The acts of just one partner, even unauthorized acts in many cases, bind all the partners.

5. An individual partnership interest cannot be easily sold or disposed of.

6. Most tax-supported fringe benefits like pension and profit-sharing arrangements available to corporations are unavailable to partnerships.

# LIMITED LIABILITY COMPANY (LLC)

Most states have adopted laws that allow a business to operate as a limited liability corporation (LLC). In general, the objectives of an LLC are to obtain the limited liability feature of a corporation along with the tax treatment of a partnership in which income and loss items pass through to the partner with no corporate tax.

Since LLCs are a recently developed form of business and rules vary from state to state, you need to consult with an attorney to discuss the advantages and disadvantages of doing business as an LLC.

# CORPORATION

A corporation is a business that is formed and authorized by state law to act as a single entity, although it is constituted and owned by one or more persons. It is legally endowed with rights and responsibilities and has a life of its own independent of the owners and operators. It has been defined by the United States Supreme Court as "an artificial being, invisible, intangible and existing only in contemplation of the law."

**Corporate Stock.** The stockholders of a corporation are the owners of the corporation. When a business incorporates, it issues shares indicating who owns what "share" of the incorporated business—shares (units) of stock. These stocks are paid for, in turn, with money, property, or services. Thus, if a corporation's net worth is $30,000 and there are 300 shares issued, then each share is worth $100. And if there is a total of two persons each of whom owns 150 shares of the stock, then each person (shareholder) owns half or 50% of the corporation.

There are two main types of stock which a corporation may issue: common stock and preferred stock.

Common Stocks: The holders of the common stocks are entitled to have the primary voice (usually by voting rights with each share of stock having one vote) in picking the directors, the principal policy-makers of a corporation. Furthermore, they are entitled to share in the profits and in a final distribution of the corporate assets on dissolution.

More than one kind ("class") of common stock may be issued, with certain conditions imposed upon each class, such as restrictions on voting rights. These become designated by "class" in terms of what rights they may be entitled to: Class A-voting stock, Class B-non-voting stock, etc.

Preferred Stocks: The holders of the preferred stocks are usually entitled to have some "preference" over the holders of common stocks with respect to receipt of dividends and distribution of assets on dissolution. They usually do not have voting rights, however. Preferred shares are generally not issued by smaller corporations.

For our purposes in this manual and for the purposes of most small or medium-sized corporations, only one type of stock is relevant—common stock. One class of common stock generally serves the needs and purposes of most small corporations.

The most important thing for a small or medium-sized corporation to remember is that it isn't really necessary to authorize or issue a large number of shares of (common) stock or more than one class of stock. The "minimum" number of shares allowed under the particular state's laws will be sufficient for most of its purposes. Beyond this "minimum," the state usually imposes a proportionately higher filing fee and taxes, and matters begin to get confusing and unnecessarily complicated.

Moreover, a "no-par value" (common) stock will suffice for most practical needs of the average small or medium-sized corporation. Hence, no-par shares are increasingly being issued by most corporations.

No-Par Value Stock: A so-called no-par value stock bears no stated or nominal value on the face of the stock certificate; hence, it does not purport to represent anything more than the given number of shares or ownership interest in the corporation. The actual value represented by the stock will depend, therefore, on what an investor is willing to pay for it, based on such factors as: the product line of the corporation, the assets it owns, the profitability of its business, the quality of its management, its record of past performance and dividend payouts, etc.

Par Value Stock: A so-called par value stock, on the other hand, bears a stated or nominal value on the face of the stock certificate (i.e. 1¢), which represents the price below which a corporation cannot legally issue its shares. However, merely because a share of stock has a par value of 1¢ does not necessarily mean that is what the stock is actually worth. In fact, the concept of par value has no actual connection with the price paid for a share of stock in an arm's length transaction. Rather, the value of any share of stock fluctuates daily based on market demand on any particular day. Thus, it is misleading to measure the actual worth of a stock based on its par value.

**The Advantages of a Corporation.** The advantages of a corporation include:

1. Limited liability; that is, the owners are liable for debts and obligations of the corporation only to the extent of their investment in the corporation, with the exception that they can be personally liable for certain types of taxes such as payroll taxes which have been withheld from the employees' paychecks but not paid over to the Internal Revenue Service or to the state income taxing authority and state sales taxes. If the business fails or loses a lawsuit, the general creditors cannot attach the owners' homes, cars and other personal property.

2. Capital can be raised more easily than in other forms of ownership, though corporate status is no guarantee of unlimited funding. A new corporation may have difficulty selling stock. In the first place the sale of stock is highly regulated by both federal and state governments, and obtaining bank loans for a fledgling business may be no easier for a new corporation than for a partnership or proprietorship.

3. Ownership is more easily transferable. This includes transferring shares to family members as gifts or for other purposes as well as selling an interest to some other person. However, in many small corporations it is advisable to put restrictions on transfer of shares especially if the persons owning and

working in the business must be able to work closely together. This is generally done by means of a stockholders' agreement.

4. Since the corporation is an independent legal entity, it has a life of its own or continuous existence. It does not cease just because one of the owners dies or wishes to retire.

5. There is centralized management which usually rests in the board of directors and is exercised by the officers.

6. As a legal entity, a corporation can enter into contracts, can sue, and can be sued. The consent and signature of the owners is not necessary for the transaction of business.

7. Salaries are normally set at the beginning of the fiscal year, so corporations have a built-in impetus to increase the capital by reinvesting it. Salaries are tied to earnings and growth, so responsible management is encouraged. In addition, surplus earnings can be set aside for a future date, although there are federal tax penalties if these surpluses exceed certain amounts.

8. Many companies offer discounts to corporations, an indication that they favor corporate accounts.

9. Retirement funds such as Keogh, defined-contribution plans, money purchase plans, and other profit-sharing, pension and stock option plans offer benefits to corporations that are not available to other businesses.

*The disadvantages of a corporation include:*

1. It is subject to more governmental regulations than are partnerships and sole proprietorships.

2. It is the most expensive form of business to organize.

3. There is double taxation, since both the corporate entity and the individual owners have to file tax returns and pay taxes.

4. Record-keeping requirements can be very extensive.

5. Operating across state lines can be complicated because of the need for corporations to "qualify to do business" in states where they are not incorporated.

6. Ending the corporate existence, and in many cases even changing some of the structure of it, requires an amendment to the certificate of incorporation, which can be more complicated and costly than for partnerships and sole proprietorships.

While the selection of the form of organization should be decided with professional assistance, the prevailing attitude is that a corporation is the preferred form of organization with its advantages far outweighing its disadvantages. That explains why over 33 percent of all American businesses are incorporated.

# STATE AND LOCAL REQUIREMENTS
# FOR CREATING A CORPORATION

Once you have decided that the corporation is the form of organization you wish to utilize for a business, you must go through the legal steps required to create this entity. These steps vary from state to state and vary in complexity. With careful planning, most people can easily create a corporation without a lawyer, saving hundreds of dollars in legal fees.

Not only should the parties starting a new business look into the formalities of incorporation, but other possible regulation and clearances must also be considered. Permits and licenses are required for such businesses as real estate brokers, barbers, hairdressers, private investigators, cosmetologists, billiard rooms, pharmacies, nursing homes, notaries, peddlers, newsstands, employment agencies, businesses serving or selling alcoholic beverages, health concerns and hospitals, and educational institutions. Many businesses, such as brokerage and securities businesses, air transportation, banking, and drug manufacturing companies, are regulated by federal agencies. Before commencing any new business, you should consider what regulations are applicable so that your business will not be conducted in violation of these rules and regulations.

In addition, any business that hires employees must take into account that it is subject to rules relating to withholding local, state and federal taxes and that it must pay social security tax, unemployment insurance and worker's compensation. It must consider whether any unions have jurisdiction and what pension or other payments must be made to them. Minimum wage requirements and their applicability should be considered together with the permissibility of hiring minors and any occupational safety and health regulations.

There are a number of federal and local agencies besides the office of the Secretary of State that can assist you in starting your new business (or incorporating your old one). First are your state Department of Securities and the regional office of the Securities and Exchange Commission. These agencies regulate the sale of securities. In most start-ups of small businesses, the owners of stock are so few that neither the state nor federal governments need be involved. They usually become involved only when you are selling stock to a large number of people (usually over 25) or making what is known as a "public offering." However, even if you have fewer than 25 stockholders, you should find out whether your stock sale or your proposed financing must be cleared with the authorities.

The Small Business Administration of the federal government was established by Congress in 1953 to assist small businesses. This agency provides prospective, new, and established members of the small business community with financial and management training and counseling. Check your yellow pages for the local office. Counseling sponsored by the Service Corps of Retired Executives (SCORE) is extremely helpful, and this organization may offer free on-site counseling services and free workshops and seminars. Also contact your local trade associations and the local chamber of commerce. They too can give you much advice and assistance.

# WHERE TO INCORPORATE

The first question to decide is the state within which to organize the corporation. There are fifty states and the District of Columbia to choose from. You may have heard of the advantages of incorporating in the State of Delaware, and it is true that a great percentage of the publicly held corporations in this country are incorporated there. There are reasons for this, but many of these do not make sense for small corporations. As a matter of fact, many of these large Delaware corporations started out in other states and only when they grew in size to become large national incorporations moved their "corporate entity" to Delaware.

Decide what state to incorporate in based on relevant business factors. The location of your actual physical facilities can be the most important factor. A second factor is the cost of incorporating in that state, or if you incorporate in some other state, what it will cost to become authorized to do business in the state where you are located. These costs include fees to check and reserve the name you want to use for your corporation, the cost of filing incorporation papers, and whether there is a one-time organizational fee or franchise tax. (This is often based upon the number of shares you will have authorized for the corporation to issue.) If you need to be authorized to do business in another state, the filing fees, name reservation fees, and initial franchise fees should be determined and considered. In addition to the initial costs, you must determine whether there are subsequent annual fees in the states you are considering. For example, is there an annual report to file with the Secretary of State? What is the filing fee? Is there an annual franchise tax? Is there a state or local income tax, and if so, how is it calculated?

States generally require that a corporation incorporated within them must maintain a registered agent in the state in order to receive communications and to be available to receive summons in law suits and other document service. Generally, this agent may be the office of the corporation itself, so if you are physically in the state of incorporation, the corporation itself, or an officer thereof, may be the registered agent. If you incorporate in a state where you do not actually have an office, you need to have an agent there, and there are many organizations in the business of representing corporations for an annual fee. These organizations are easily located in law directories. The cost of a registered agent must be an additional consideration entering your decision as to state of incorporation.

Further considerations involved in the decision of where to incorporate include whether the laws covering corporations in your state of choice are beneficial to the corporation. For example, some states require three incorporators and three directors. If you plan to have a corporation that only one person is going to own or control, your state might require you to have more board members than you need or want. The discussion in this book about what goes into the certificate of incorporation will cover many of these items which vary from state to state. Before you make the final decision on the location of your corporation, you should obtain a copy of the corporation statutes and read them so that you can identify and evaluate obstacles. These statutes can be found in public libraries and in law libraries. In many instances, the Secretary of State's office will make them available free or for a small charge. The *Martindale-Hubbell Law Directory,* which can be found in many libraries, contains summaries of the laws of all fifty states. Even with the forms included in this book you should read the statutes before filing incorporation papers.

Once you have decided what state to incorporate in, a great deal of information about how to set up that corporation can be obtained from the appropriate Secretary of State. The following is a listing of the addresses and telephone numbers of persons to contact in the various states.

**ALABAMA**
Secretary of State
State Capitol
Montgomery, Alabama 36130
(205/242-7200)

**ALASKA**
State of Alaska
Department of Commerce and Economic Development
Corporations
Juneau, Alaska 99811-0808
(907/465-2530)

**ARIZONA**
Arizona Corporation Commission
Information Division
2222 West Encanto Boulevard
Phoenix, Arizona 85009
(602/542-3076)

**ARKANSAS**
Secretary of State
State Capitol
Little Rock, Arkansas 72201
(501/682-1010)

**CALIFORNIA**
Secretary of State
1230 J Street
Sacramento, California 95814
(916/445-0620)

**COLORADO**
Secretary of State
1560 Broadway, Suite 200
Denver, Colorado 80202
(303/894-2251)

**CONNECTICUT**
Office of the Secretary of State
State of Connecticut
30 Trinity Street
Hartford, Connecticut 06106
(203/566-8570)

**DELAWARE**
State of Delaware
Department of State
Division of Incorporations
Townsend Building
P.O. Box 898
Dover, Delaware 19903
(302/739-3073)

**DISTRICT OF COLUMBIA**
Corporations Division
614 H Street, N.W.
Room 407
Washington, D.C. 20001
(202/727-7283)

**FLORIDA**
Division of Corporations
P.O. Box 6327
Tallahassee, Florida 32314
(904/488-9000)

**GEORGIA**
Secretary of State
Business Services and Regulations
Suite 315, West Tower
2 Martin Luther King, Jr. Drive, S.E.
Atlanta, Georgia 30334
(404/656-2185)

**HAWAII**
Commerce and Consumer Affairs
Business Registration
P.O. Box 40
Honolulu, Hawaii 96810
(808/586-2727)

**IDAHO**
Secretary of State
State of Idaho
P.O. Box 83720
Boise, Idaho 83720-0080
(208/334-2300)

**INDIANA**
Secretary of State
Corporations Division
219 State House
Indianapolis, Indiana 46204
(317/232-6576)

**IOWA**
Secretary of State
State Capitol/Corporations Division
Hoover Building
Des Moines, Iowa 50319
(515/281-5204)

**KANSAS**
State of Kansas
Secretary of State
The State House
300 S.W. 10th Avenue, 2nd Floor
Topeka, Kansas 66612-1594
(913/296-2236)

**KENTUCKY**
Secretary of State
Capitol Building, Corporation Division
Frankfort, Kentucky 40601
(502/564-7330)

**LOUISIANA**
Secretary of State
P.O. Box 94125
Baton Rouge, Louisiana 70804
(504/925-4704)

**MAINE**
Secretary of State
State of Maine
Department of State
Augusta, Maine 04333
(207/626-8400)

**MARYLAND**
State Department of Assessments and Taxation
301 West Preston Street
Baltimore, Maryland 21201
(410/333-4616)

**MASSACHUSETTS**
Secretary of State
Corporations Division
1 Ashburton Place, 17th Floor
Boston, Massachusetts 02108
(617/727-9640)

**MICHIGAN**
State of Michigan
Department of Commerce
Corporation Division
P.O. Box 30054
Lansing, Michigan 48909
(517/334-6206)

**MINNESOTA**
Secretary of State
180 State Office Building
St. Paul, Minnesota 55155
(612/296-3266)

**MISSISSIPPI**
Secretary of State
P.O. Box 136
Jackson, Mississippi 39205
(601/359-1333)

**MISSOURI**
Secretary of State
P.O. Box 778
Jefferson City, Missouri 65101
(314/751-4153)

**MONTANA**
Secretary of State
P.O. Box 202801
Helena, Montana 59620-2801
(406/444-2034)

**NEBRASKA**
Secretary of State
P.O. Box 94608
Lincoln, Nebraska 68509
(402/471-4079)

**NEVADA**
Secretary of State
Capitol Complex
Carson City, Nevada 89710
(702/687-5203)

**NEW HAMPSHIRE**
Department of Revenue Administration
Document Processing Division
P.O. Box 637
Concord, New Hampshire 03302
(603/271-2186)

**NEW JERSEY**
State of New Jersey
Department of State
CN 308
Trenton, New Jersey 08625
(609/530-6400)

**NEW MEXICO**
State Corporation Commission
Franchise Tax Department
P.O. Drawer 1269
Santa Fe, New Mexico 87501
(505/827-4500)

**NEW YORK**
Department of State
Division of Corporations
162 Washington Avenue
Albany, New York 12231
(518/473-2492)

**NORTH CAROLINA**
Secretary of State
Raleigh, North Carolina 27603
(919/733-4201)

**NORTH DAKOTA**
Secretary of State
Capitol Building
600 East Boulevard
Bismarck, North Dakota 58505
(701/224-4284)

**OHIO**
Secretary of State
30 East Broad Street, 14th Floor
Columbus, Ohio 43266-0418
(614/466-2655)

**OKLAHOMA**
Secretary of State
101 State Capitol Building
Oklahoma City, Oklahoma 73105
(405/521-3911)

**OREGON**
Corporation Division
Business Registry
255 Capitol Street, N.E., Suite 151
Commerce Building
Salem, Oregon 97310-1327
(503/986-2200)

**PENNSYLVANIA**
Commonwealth of Pennsylvania
Department of State
Corporation Division
Harrisburg, Pennsylvania 17105
(717/787-1057)

**RHODE ISLAND**
Secretary of State
State House
Corporation Division
Providence, Rhode Island 02903
(401/277-3040)

**SOUTH CAROLINA**
Secretary of State
P.O. Box 11350
Columbia, South Carolina 29211
(803/734-2158)

**SOUTH DAKOTA**
Secretary of State
Corporation Division
500 East Capitol Avenue
Pierre, South Dakota 57501
(605/773-4845)

**TENNESSEE**
Secretary of State
Division of Services
James K. Polk Building, Suite 1800
Nashville, Tennessee 37243-0306
(615/741-2286)

**TEXAS**
Secretary of State
Corporation Division
1019 Brazos Street
Austin, Texas 78701
(512/463-5555)

**UTAH**
Secretary of State
Division of Corporations
P.O. Box 45801
Salt Lake City, Utah 84145-0801
(801/530-4849)

**VERMONT**
Secretary of State
Corporation Division
109 State Street
Montpelier, Vermont 05609-1104
(802/828-2386)

**VIRGINIA**
Commonwealth of Virginia
State Corporation Commission
John Tyler Building
1300 E. Main Street
P.O. Box 1197
Richmond, Virginia 23209
(804/371-9967)

**WASHINGTON**
Secretary of State
Corporation Division
P.O. Box 40234
Olympia, Washington 98504-0234
(206/753-7120)

**WEST VIRGINIA**
Secretary of State
State Capitol W-139
Corporation Division
Charleston, West Virginia 25305
(304/558-8000)

**WISCONSIN**
Secretary of State
Corporation Division
P.O. Box 7846
Madison, Wisconsin 53707
(608/266-3590)

**WYOMING**
Secretary of State
The Capitol
Cheyenne, Wyoming 82002-0020
(307-777-7311)

# TAX ASPECTS OF INCORPORATION

The subject of corporate taxes is beyond the primary scope of this manual. However, a few words about the subject of taxation should be mentioned. Beyond that, it is necessary for the owners of a new corporation to consult an attorney or accountant about setting up a comprehensive tax plan to meet their particular needs.

The owners of a corporation can elect to pay taxes in one of two ways. They may decide to do business as a regular "C" corporation and have the corporation pay taxes at corporate tax rates, or they can elect treatment as a co-called S corporation (formerly called a "Subchapter S" corporation). With a C corporation, not only does the corporation pay corporate income tax, but the stockholders also pay tax on income received from the corporation. Electing S corporation status allows owners to have the corporation's income and deductions passed through to them and to pay the taxes individually at personal tax rates.

What are the advantages of electing S corporation status? Briefly, S corporation status legally allows business owners the regular advantages of doing business as a corporation while still being taxed as individuals.

Shareholders may elect S corporation status if the corporation meets the following requirements.

1. It is a domestic U.S. corporation.

2. It has no more than 35 shareholders (stocks owned jointly, in common, or in their separate names by a husband and wife are treated as owned by one shareholder).

3. It has only individuals, estates, or certain trusts as shareholders.

4. It has no shareholders who are nonresident aliens.

5. It has only one class of stock.

6. The election to become an S Corporation has the consent of all the shareholders.

7. It is not a member of a so-called affiliated corporate group, nor is it a bank, insurance company, a "possessions" corporation, or a domestic international sales corporation — as defined in Section 1361 of the Internal Revenue Code.

If you want to elect treatment as an S corporation, you must complete and file with the IRS a simple form, IRS Form 2553, permitting filing as a small business corporation. Form 2553 must be filed by the 15th day of the third month of the first taxable year. S corporations generally must adopt the calendar year as their tax year, but there is some leeway in electing a fiscal year, as explained in the instructions to Form 2553.

Each year thereafter, the corporation must file an S corporation tax return with the IRS on Form 1120S. This form shows the corporate income and losses that are passed through to the shareholders. The S corporation gives each shareholder a copy of the Schedule K-1 of Form 1120S, showing his or her individual share of the corporation's income and deductions.

The decision to elect treatment as an S corporation can provide benefits, but whether it is the right choice for you and the other owners depends on a comparison of individual and corporate tax brackets as well as many other factors. You should discuss the entire tax situation with an attorney or accountant who is familiar with the tax rules for corporations.

# THE CERTIFICATE OR
# ARTICLES OF INCORPORATION

Many states will supply you with a blank form or with a model form which must be re-typed. Among the items of information which may be required in a certificate of incorporation are the following:

1. Name of the corporation (check for availability of the name before filing the form);

2. Proposed fiscal year;

3. Purposes of the corporation;

4. County within the state in which the corporation's office will be located;

5. Aggregate number of shares authorized for issuance, the par value of shares, and the classes of shares if more than one class;

6. Preferences, limitations, and relative rights of shares;

7. Sum of initial capital;

8. Provisions regarding shareholders' preemptive rights, if any;

9. Lawful provisions limiting statutory corporate powers, if any;

10. Address of initial registered office and name of person serving as registered agent at that address;

11. Titles of directors constituting initial board of directors;

12. Name and address of each of the initial directors;

13. Name and address of each incorporator;

14. Duration of corporation if other than perpetual; and

15. Provisions eliminating or limiting the personal liability of corporate directors.

Of course, all of these items are unlikely to be required in the certificate in one particular state, and many of them will not apply or be appropriate in your case. Check the state statute of the state in which you plan to incorporate to make certain of requirements.

# CHECKLIST

## STEPS IN THE INCORPORATION PROCESS

1. Decide upon the form of your corporation.

2. Decide where to incorporate.

3. Select a corporate name.

4. Select a fiscal year.

5. Apply for an Employer Identification Number.

6. Draft a certificate of incorporation.

7. Sign a certificate of incorporation and file it with the Secretary of State with appropriate filing fees.

8. Hold an incorporator's meeting to elect initial directors and transact the corporation's first business.

9. Hold an organizational meeting of the initial board of directors.

10. Select a corporate seal and stock certificates and issue shares.

11. Elect officers and open bank accounts.

12. Obtain required state and local licenses and/or permits.

13. Select a registered agent, if necessary.

14. File a "doing business as" certificate, if necessary.

15. Apply for authorization to do business in other states, if necessary.

# Resolutions on Corporate Structure and Governance

# RESOLUTION OF STOCKHOLDERS OF

_____

WHEREAS, by applicable by-law provisions, the stockholders of the Company are hereby authorized to change the name of the said Company, and

WHEREAS, it is now deemed desirable to change the name of the Company, be it

RESOLVED, That the name of this Corporation be changed from

to                                                           ,

and that the officers of the Company are directed to file in the public offices the requisite documents setting forth the change of name.

I certify that I am the duly elected and qualified Secretary, and that the above is a true and correct copy of a resolution duly adopted at a meeting of the Board of Directors thereof, convened and held in accordance with law and the By-laws of said Corporation on                          , 19      , and that such resolution is now in full force and effect.

IN WITNESS WHEREOF, I have affixed my name as Secretary and have caused the corporate seal of said Corporation to be hereunto affixed this

day of                          , 19      .


A True Record

Attest

_____

Secretary

# RESOLUTION OF BOARD OF DIRECTORS OF

_____

That at a meeting of the Board of Directors duly called and held at the office of

the Corporation on                         , 19        , whereupon a quorum of the Board

was present, it was

RESOLVED, That it is desirable to amend the Articles of Incorporation as

follows:

RESOLVED FURTHER, That a special meeting of the stockholders of this

Corporation is hereby called, to be held at                                              , on

             , 19        at        .m. to vote upon this recommendation and that

the Secretary shall give notice of such meeting to the stockholders in accordance with

the Articles and By-laws of the Corporation.

I certify that I am the duly elected and qualified Secretary of the Corporation,

and that the above is a true and correct copy of a resolution duly adopted at said meeting.

IN WITNESS WHEREOF, I have affixed my name as Secretary and have

caused the corporate seal of said Corporation to be hereunto affixed this

day of                         , 19        .


A True Record

Attest

_____

                                          Secretary

# RESOLUTION OF STOCKHOLDERS OF

_____

WHEREAS, the Board of Directors of the Corporation recommended that the Articles of Incorporation of the Corporation be changed as hereinafter set forth, and

WHEREAS, the stockholders of the Corporation approve said proposed amendment.

RESOLVED, That the Articles of Incorporation of the said Corporation be changed, as follows:

RESOLVED FURTHER, That the Chairman and Secretary of this meeting are directed to execute and acknowledge a certificate under the corporate seal of this Corporation, reciting the foregoing resolution, and to file and record said certificate in the manner required by law.

RESOLVED FURTHER, That, upon recording said amendment, a duplicate shall be placed in the minutes.

I certify that I am the duly elected and qualified Secretary, and that the above is a true and correct copy of a resolution duly adopted at said meeting held on                                   ,

19       , and that such resolution is now in full force and effect.

IN WITNESS WHEREOF, I have affixed my name as Secretary and have caused the corporate seal of said Corporation to be hereunto affixed this

day of                         , 19       .

A True Record

Attest

_____

Secretary

# CERTIFICATE OF STOCKHOLDERS' CONSENT OF

_____

        We, the undersigned, being stockholders of

Corporation, hereby consent to the adoption of the amendment to the Articles of

Incorporation as contained in the directors' resolution of          , 19     ,

which amendment reads as follows:

and signify our consent:

|                Stockholder                |     Number of Shares     |
| ----------------------------------------- | ------------------------ |
| _____   | _____    |
| _____   | _____    |
| _____   | _____    |
| _____   | _____    |
| _____   | _____    |
| _____   | _____    |
| _____   | _____    |

A True Record

Attest

_____

        Secretary

# CERTIFICATE OF AMENDMENT

That the above Corporation of the State of                          , whose

principal office is located at                          , certifies

that at a meeting of the stockholders of said Corporation called for the purpose of

amending the Articles of Incorporation, and held on                          , 19        , it

was resolved by the vote of the holders of sufficient shares of each class entitled to vote

that the Articles of Incorporation be amended to read as follows:

Signed with the corporate seal affixed this                          , 19        .

A True Record

Attest

_____
President

_____
Secretary

# RESOLUTION OF STOCKHOLDERS OF

_____

RESOLVED, That the Board of Directors of the Corporation is authorized to amend, alter, change, suspend, add to, repeal, or rescind any and all By-laws of said Corporation from time to time as they, in their judgment deem proper, without action or consent on the part of the stockholders, and

RESOLVED, FURTHER, That the stockholders reserve the right to revoke the above authority by resolution duly passed at any future stockholder meeting.

I certify that I am the duly elected and qualified Secretary, and that the above is a true and correct copy of a resolution duly adopted at a meeting of the stockholders thereof, convened and held in accordance with law and the By-laws of said Corporation on                        , 19       , and that such resolution is now in full force and effect.

IN WITNESS WHEREOF, I have affixed my name as Secretary and have caused the corporate seal of said Corporation to be hereunto affixed this

day of                   , 19       .


A True Record

Attest

                                                _____

                                                Secretary

# CERTIFICATE OF STOCKHOLDERS' CONSENT

We, the undersigned, stockholders of the Corporation, at a meeting held pursuant to notice at the office of the Corporation, on                    , 19          , at          .m., to take action upon the following resolution adopted at a meeting of the Board of Directors of the Corporation, held on                    , 19       :

consent in writing that the amendment to the By-laws as stated in the Directors' resolution, be adopted.

| Names | Proxies | No. of Shares |
|-------|---------|---------------|
| _____ | _____ | _____ |
| _____ | _____ | _____ |
| _____ | _____ | _____ |
| _____ | _____ | _____ |
| _____ | _____ | _____ |
| _____ | _____ | _____ |

A True Record

Attest

_____
Secretary

# RESOLUTION OF BOARD OF DIRECTORS OF

_____

RESOLVED, That the Board of Directors of the Corporation deemed it advisable to amend the By-laws to read as follows:

RESOLVED FURTHER, That a special meeting of the stockholders of this Corporation is called to be held at the office of the Corporation at

, on

, 19          , at               .m., to consider and vote upon the foregoing resolution, and that the Secretary of the Corporation is directed to give notice of the said meeting to stockholders of the Corporation.

I certify that I am the duly elected and qualified Secretary, and that the above is a true and correct copy of a resolution duly adopted at a meeting of the Board of Directors held in accordance with the law and the By-laws of said Corporation on                          ,

19       , and that such resolution remains in full force and effect.

IN WITNESS WHEREOF, I have affixed my name as Secretary and have caused the corporate seal of said Corporation to be hereunto affixed this

day of                     , 19       .

A True Record

Attest

_____
Secretary

# RESOLUTION OF STOCKHOLDERS OF

RESOLVED, That the authorized capital stock of the Corporation be increased from its present number of                    shares to consist of                    shares of the par value of

Dollars ($                    ) each, and

RESOLVED FURTHER, That the Articles of Organization or the Certificate of incorporation of this Corporation be amended to read as follows:



RESOLVED FURTHER, That the President and the Secretary of this Corporation are authorized to sign and acknowledge the certificates of proceedings required by law, to file such certificates in the appropriate public office, and to perform all acts that may be necessary or proper to carry into effect the foregoing resolution in compliance with the laws of the State of                    .

I certify that I am the duly elected and qualified Secretary, and that the above is a true and correct copy of a resolution duly adopted at a meeting convened and held in accordance with law and the By-laws of said Corporation on                    ,

19          , and that such resolution is now in full force and effect.

IN WITNESS WHEREOF, I have affixed my name as Secretary and have caused the corporate seal of said Corporation to be hereunto affixed this

day of                    , 19          .

A True Record

Attest

_____

Secretary

# RESOLUTION OF BOARD OF DIRECTORS OF

_____

RESOLVED, That this Board of Directors deems it advisable and for the benefit of its stockholders that said Corporation be dissolved; and to that end, as required by law, it is ordered that a meeting of those stockholders of said Corporation having voting power to take action upon this resolution be called and held at the office of said Corporation, at                              ,                              ,

on                    , 19    , at              .m., and

RESOLVED, FURTHER, That the Secretary of this Corporation is directed to cause notice of the adoption of this resolution to be mailed to each stockholder of this Corporation.

I certify that I am the duly elected and qualified Secretary, and that the above is a true and correct copy of a resolution duly adopted at a meeting of the Board of Directors thereof, convened and held in accordance with law and the By-laws of said Corporation on                    , 19    , and that such resolution is now in full force and effect.

IN WITNESS WHEREOF, I have affixed my name as Secretary and have caused the corporate seal of said Corporation to be hereunto affixed this day of                    , 19    .


A True Record

Attest

_____

Secretary

# RESOLUTION OF STOCKHOLDERS OF

RESOLVED, That                              dissolve its
charter to the State of                              and that it cease to exist as a
corporation, and

RESOLVED, FURTHER, That                              the President,
and                              , the Secretary, of

, are directed to file the necessary certificate of dissolution of this
Corporation with the Secretary of the State of                              , and such other
official office as may be required by law, and

RESOLVED, FURTHER, That the Board of Directors of this Corporation is
hereby authorized, empowered, and directed to do all things necessary to settle the
affairs of the Corporation, to collect the outstanding debts, to provide for the payment of
the liabilities and obligations of the Corporation, to distribute its assets, and to do all
other things necessary to carry into effect the foregoing resolution.

I certify that I am the duly elected and qualified Secretary and that the above is a
true and correct copy of a resolution duly organized at a meeting of the stockholders
thereof, convened and held in accordance with law and the By-laws of said Corporation
on                              , 19      , and that such resolution is now in full force and effect.

IN WITNESS WHEREOF, I have affixed my name as Secretary and have
caused the corporate seal of said Corporation to be hereunto affixed this
day of                              , 19      .

A True Record

Attest

_____
Secretary

# AFFIDAVIT OF SECRETARY OF

State of

                , SS:

County of

                           , being duly sworn, deposes and says:

1.      That he/she is the Secretary of                 , a corporation duly existing under the laws of the State of              .

2.      That he/she is the custodian of the stock book of said corporation.

3.      That the total number of shares of the capital stock of the said corporation issued and outstanding on         , 19    , is          shares, and that the persons whose signatures are affixed to the foregoing consent are the holders of more than a majority of said capital stock so issued and outstanding as of said date.

A True Record

Attest

                                  _____

                                      Secretary

Sworn to before me this            day of                , 19    .

                                  _____

                                      Notary Public

# CERTIFICATE OF DISSOLUTION

We, the President and Secretary of                                        in accordance

with the requirements of the Corporation Laws of the State of

in order to obtain the dissolution of said Corporation, as provided by said Law

DO CERTIFY AS FOLLOWS:

The registered office of

(Corporation) in the State of                                        is at

,                                                  , and the resident

agent thereof, upon whom process against this Corporation may be served, is

,                                                  ,

.


Dissolution of said Corporation has been duly authorized in accordance with the

provisions of the Corporation Laws of the State of                                        .

Following is a list of the names and residence addresses of the directors of the

Corporation:

Name                                        Address

Following is a list of the names and residence addresses of the officers of the
Corporation:

| Name | Office | Residence |
|------|--------|-----------|

A True Record

Attest

                                      _____

                                      President

                                      _____

                                      Secretary

# Resolutions on Major Corporate Actions

# RESOLUTION OF BOARD OF DIRECTORS OF

_____

RESOLVED, That the President of this Corporation is hereby authorized to enter

into a contract with                                                    , employing

                                        to act as accountants and

auditors for this Corporation for a period of                              commencing

on                              , 19        , at a yearly compensation not to exceed

                                        Dollars ($                ).

I certify that I am the duly elected and qualified Secretary and that the above is a

true and correct copy of a resolution duly adopted at a meeting of the Board of Directors

thereof, convened and held in accordance with the law and the By-laws of said

Corporation on                              , 19        , and that such resolution is now in full

force and effect.

IN WITNESS WHEREOF, I have affixed my name as Secretary and have

caused the corporate seal of said Corporation to be hereunto affixed this

day of                        , 19        .


A True Record

Attest


_____

Secretary

# RESOLUTION OF BOARD OF DIRECTORS OF

_____

      RESOLVED, That

are appointed attorneys and counsel for the Corporation and that their customary

professional charges for their services be paid to them from time to time as billed.

      I certify that I am the duly elected and qualified Secretary and that the above is a

true and correct copy of a resolution duly adopted at a meeting of the Board of Directors

thereof, convened and held in accordance with the law and the By-laws of said

Corporation on               , 19    , and that such resolution is now in full

force and effect.

      IN WITNESS WHEREOF, I have affixed my name as secretary and have

caused the corporate seal of said Corporation to be hereunto affixed this

day of           , 19    .


A True Record

Attest

                              _____

                              Secretary

# RESOLUTION OF BOARD OF DIRECTORS OF

_____

RESOLVED, That                                          , attorney

for this Corporation, commence suit for this Corporation for its claim against

                                        with authority to settle the claim at

such amount and upon such terms as are in the best interest of this Corporation, provided

that the President of the Corporation concurs.

I certify that I am the duly elected and qualified Secretary, and that the above is a

true and correct copy of a resolution duly adopted at a meeting of the Board of Directors

thereof, convened and held in accordance with the law and the By-laws of said

Corporation on                            , 19      , and that such resolution is now in full

force and effect.

IN WITNESS WHEREOF, I have affixed my name as secretary and have

caused the corporate seal of said Corporation to be hereunto affixed this

day of                            , 19      .


A True Record

Attest

                                        _____

                                        Secretary

# RESOLUTION OF STOCKHOLDERS OF

_____

WHEREAS, this Corporation desires to borrow for its general corporate purposes, be it

RESOLVED, That the Board of Directors of this Corporation is authorized to borrow, from time to time, such sums as it may deem advisable upon the notes of this Corporation and for that purpose to pledge any assets of the Corporation to secure such notes.

I certify that I am the duly elected and qualified Secretary, and that the above is a true and correct copy of a resolution duly adopted at a meeting of the Board of Directors thereof, convened and held in accordance with the law and the By-laws of said Corporation on                            , 19       , and that such resolution is now in full force and effect.

IN WITNESS WHEREOF, I have affixed my name as secretary and have caused the corporate seal of said Corporation to be hereunto affixed this
day of                       , 19       .


A True Record

Attest

                                        _____

                                        Secretary

# RESOLUTION OF BOARD OF DIRECTORS OF

_____

RESOLVED, That                                        , the

Corporation, be authorized, in the name of and

for the account of this Corporation and on such terms and conditions as he/they may

deem proper to borrow from                        (Bank) any and all sums

of money; to sign, execute, and endorse such documents as may be necessary or required

by said Bank to evidence such indebtedness; to discount or rediscount with said Bank

any of the bills receivable held by this Corporation; to apply for and obtain from said

Bank letters of credit and to sign and execute agreements to secure said Bank with any

assets of the Corporation in connection therewith; to pledge and/or mortgage any

moneys on deposit or in the possession of said Bank, and/or any bonds, stocks, bills

receivable, or other property of this Corporation, to secure the payment of any

indebtedness, liability or obligation of this Corporation to said Bank whether due or to

become due and whether existing or hereafter incurred however arising; to withdraw

and/or substitute any property of this Corporation held at any time by said Bank; and

generally to do and perform all acts and sign all agreements, obligations, pledges, and/or

other instruments necessary or required by said Bank for its protection in its dealings

with this Corporation, and

RESOLVED, FURTHER, That all banking transactions by any of the officers or

representatives of this Corporation in its name and for its account with said Bank prior to

this meeting are approved and ratified, and

RESOLVED, FURTHER, That said Bank be furnished with a certified copy of

these resolutions, and it be authorized to deal with the officers hereinabove named under

said authority until expressly notified in writing to the contrary.

I certify that I am the duly elected and qualified Secretary and that the above is a true and correct copy of a resolution duly adopted at a meeting of the Board of Directors thereof, convened and held in accordance with the law and the By-laws of said Corporation on                    , 19     , and that such resolution is now in full force and effect.

IN WITNESS WHEREOF, I have affixed my name as secretary and have caused the corporate seal of said Corporation to be hereunto affixed this day of                , 19     .


A True Record

Attest

_____

                           Secretary

# RESOLUTION OF BOARD OF DIRECTORS OF

_____

RESOLVED, That this Corporation sell real estate located in

,

, more particularly described as:

to                              (Buyer), for                    Dollars ($              );

and that the President of this Corporation in behalf of the Corporation shall execute and

deliver said deed and other instruments as may be required in connection therewith and

shall affix the corporate seal of this Corporation thereto.

RESOLVED, FURTHER, That the purchase agreement presented to this

meeting, a copy of which is annexed, be approved with such changes as the officers

executing same on behalf of this Corporation may, with the advice of counsel, approve.

I certify that I am the duly elected and qualified Secretary and that the above is a true and correct copy of a resolution duly adopted at a meeting of the Board of Directors thereof, convened and held in accordance with the law and the By-laws of said Corporation on _____ , 19 ___ , and that such resolution is now in full force and effect.

IN WITNESS WHEREOF, I have affixed my name as secretary and have caused the corporate seal of said Corporation to be hereunto affixed this _____ day of _____ , 19 ___ .

A True Record

Attest

_____
                                    Secretary

# RESOLUTION OF BOARD OF DIRECTORS OF

_____

WHEREAS,            , owner of real estate at

           ,            , City

of            , State of            , has offered to

sell said property to this Corporation for the sum of            Dollars

($            ), upon the terms hereinafter set forth, and

WHEREAS, the Board of Directors deems it advisable that the Corporation

purchase said land and building from            for said price,

be it

RESOLVED, That this Corporation purchase from           

the land and building more specifically described as:

RESOLVED, FURTHER, That the President of this Corporation is authorized to enter into an agreement on behalf of this Corporation with said Seller to purchase the above property pursuant to the agreement annexed.

RESOLVED, FURTHER, That the President of this Corporation is authorized to execute all documents and make all payments necessary to carry out the foregoing resolution and to accept all documents, duly executed, which may be necessary for the transfer and conveyance to this Corporation.

I certify that I am the duly elected and qualified Secretary and that the above is a true and correct copy of a resolution duly adopted at a meeting of the Board of Directors thereof, convened and held in accordance with the law and the By-laws of said Corporation on                        , 19        , and that such resolution is now in full force and effect.

IN WITNESS WHEREOF, I have affixed my name as secretary and have caused the corporate seal of said Corporation to be hereunto affixed this day of                 , 19        .


A True Record

Attest

_____

                        Secretary

# RESOLUTION OF BOARD OF DIRECTORS OF

_____

RESOLVED, That this Company enter into a lease from

, for the premises at                                             ,

,                                      , for a term of

years from                          , 19      , in accordance with the terms set forth and

contained in a lease presented to and read at this meeting; that the President is authorized

in behalf of the Company to execute and deliver said lease and to attach the seal of the

Company thereto, and

I certify that I am the duly elected and qualified Secretary and that the above is a

true and correct copy of a resolution duly adopted at a meeting of the Board of Directors

thereof, convened and held in accordance with the law and the By-laws of said

Corporation on                          , 19      , and that such resolution is now in full

force and effect.

IN WITNESS WHEREOF, I have affixed my name as secretary and have

caused the corporate seal of said Corporation to be hereunto affixed this

day of                      , 19      .


A True Record

Attest

_____

Secretary

# RESOLUTION OF BOARD OF DIRECTORS OF

_____

RESOLVED, That the proposed contract between this Corporation and

, submitted to this meeting, be accepted as

annexed and that                                    , President, be authorized to execute in

the name of and in behalf of this Corporation a contract substantially in the form

submitted.

I certify that I am the duly elected and qualified Secretary and that the above is a

true and correct copy of a resolution duly adopted at a meeting of the Board of Directors

thereof, convened and held in accordance with the law and the By-laws of said

Corporation on                          , 19       , and that such resolution is now in full

force and effect.

IN WITNESS WHEREOF, I have affixed my name as secretary and have

caused the corporate seal of said Corporation to be hereunto affixed this

day of                          , 19       .


A True Record

Attest


                                    _____

                                    Secretary

# RESOLUTION OF BOARD OF DIRECTORS OF

_____

RESOLVED, That the President of this Corporation be authorized to enter into a contract for                                  with the Company, in behalf of this Corporation, upon such terms and conditions as may be agreed upon between said President and said Company.

I certify that I am the duly elected and qualified Secretary and that the above is a true and correct copy of a resolution duly adopted at a meeting of the Board of Directors thereof, convened and held in accordance with the law and the By-laws of said Corporation on                          , 19      , and that such resolution is now in full force and effect.

IN WITNESS WHEREOF, I have affixed my name as secretary and have caused the corporate seal of said Corporation to be hereunto affixed this day of                     , 19      .

A True Record

Attest

_____

Secretary

# CERTIFICATE OF STOCKHOLDERS' CONSENT OF

_____

We the undersigned, stockholders of the Corporation duly organized under the

laws of the State of                                        and holders of the number of

shares set opposite our names totalling                    shares, representing the entire

capital stock of said Corporation, agree for value received and in consideration of the

same number of shares and of the same par value of the stock of

                              , to the exchange of the stock now held by us in the

Corporation for the same par value of the stock of

                              .

We the undersigned stockholders further hereby consent to the transfer of all of

the property of the Corporation to said

as existing on this date, on the agreement of said

to assume and to pay when due all the debts and obligations of said Corporation.

|              Name of Stockholder              |          Number of Shares          |
| --------------------------------------------- | ---------------------------------- |
| _____ | _____ |
| _____ | _____ |
| _____ | _____ |
| _____ | _____ |
| _____ | _____ |
| _____ | _____ |

A True Record

Attest

                                        _____

                                        Secretary

# RESOLUTION OF BOARD OF DIRECTORS OF

---

RESOLVED, That the Board of Directors of this Corporation deems it advisable to adopt the Articles of Merger, annexed, for the purpose of merging

into this Corporation.

RESOLVED, FURTHER, That a special meeting of the stockholders of this Corporation is called to be held at

on                                     , 19      , at        .m., to act upon this recommendation and that the Secretary is hereby instructed to give notice of such meeting to the stockholders in accordance with the Articles and By-laws of this Corporation.

Pursuant to the provisions of law, the undersigned corporations adopt the following Articles of Merger.

FIRST: The following Plan of Merger was approved by the shareholders of each of the undersigned corporations in the manner prescribed by law.

SECOND: As to each of the undersigned corporations, the number of shares outstanding and the designation and number of outstanding shares of each class entitled to vote as a class on such Plan are as follows:

| | | Entitled to Vote as a Class | |
|---|---|---|---|
| Name of Corporation | Number of Shares Outstanding | Designation of Class | Number of Shares |
| _____ | _____ | _____ | _____ |
| _____ | _____ | _____ | _____ |

THIRD: As to each of the undersigned corporations, the total number of shares voted for and against such Plan, respectively, and, as to each class entitled to vote thereon as a class, the number of shares of such class voted for and against such Plan, respectively, are as follows:

| Name of Corporation | Number of Shares | | Class | Entitled to Vote as a Class | |
| | Total Voted For | Total Voted Against | | Voted For | Voted Against |
| --- | --- | --- | --- | --- | --- |
| _____ | _____ | _____ | _____ | _____ | _____ |
| _____ | _____ | _____ | _____ | _____ | _____ |

Dated: _____ , 19 ___

_____

By _____

_____

By _____

_____

I certify that I am the duly elected and qualified Secretary of

_____ , a corporation organized and existing under

the laws of the State of _____ , and that the above is a true and

correct copy of a resolution duly adopted at a meeting of the Board of Directors thereof,

convened and held in accordance with the law and the By-laws of said Corporation on

_____ , 19 ___ and that such resolution is now in full force and effect.

IN WITNESS WHEREOF, I have affixed my name as secretary and have

caused the corporate seal of said Corporation to be hereunto affixed this

day of _____ , 19 ___ .

A True Record

Attest

_____
Secretary

# Resolutions on Compensation and Dividends

# RESOLUTION OF BOARD OF DIRECTORS OF

_____

WHEREAS, it is desirable for this Corporation to grant to certain employees an option to purchase stock in this Corporation, be it

RESOLVED, That in consideration of the payment of

Dollars ($              ) on account of such option, an option is hereby given for a

period of                    (                    ) years from the date hereof, to

                    , his heirs, and assigns, to purchase unissued stock of this Corporation or any part thereof.

I certify that I am the duly elected and qualified Secretary and that the above is a true and correct copy of a resolution duly adopted at a meeting of the Board of Directors thereof, convened and held in accordance with the law and the By-laws of said Corporation on                    , 19      , and that such resolution is now in full force and effect.

IN WITNESS WHEREOF, I have affixed my name as secretary and have caused the corporate seal of said Corporation to be hereunto affixed this

day of                    , 19      .


A True Record

Attest


_____

                                        Secretary

# RESOLUTION OF BOARD OF DIRECTORS OF

_____

WHEREAS,                          has rendered valuable services in behalf of this Corporation, be it

RESOLVED, That an honorarium  of            Dollars ($        ) be granted               in recognition and appreciation of the additional services so rendered, and the Treasurer of this Corporation is directed to pay the said sum to             forthwith.

I certify that I am the duly elected and qualified Secretary, and that the above is a true and correct copy of a resolution duly adopted at a meeting of the Board of Directors thereof, convened and held in accordance with the law and the By-laws of said Corporation on           , 19    , and that such resolution is now in full force and effect.

IN WITNESS WHEREOF, I have affixed my name as secretary and have caused the corporate seal of said Corporation to be hereunto affixed this day of         , 19    .

A True Record

Attest

_____

Secretary

# RESOLUTION OF BOARD OF DIRECTORS OF

_____

RESOLVED, That the Treasurer is directed to pay to each officer and employee of this Corporation who has been in its employ for a period of

(          ) months or more, a sum equal to          per cent (     %) of his or her annual salary and to each employee who has been in the employ of the Corporation for a period of less than          (          ) months, the sum of          Dollars ($          ), as additional compensation.

I certify that I am the duly elected and qualified Secretary and that the above is a true and correct copy of a resolution duly adopted at a meeting of the Board of Directors thereof, convened and held in accordance with the law and the By-laws of said Corporation on          , 19     , and that such resolution is now in full force and effect.

IN WITNESS WHEREOF, I have affixed my name as secretary and have caused the corporate seal of said Corporation to be hereunto affixed this day of          , 19     .

A True Record

Attest

_____

Secretary

# RESOLUTION OF BOARD OF DIRECTORS OF

_____

     RESOLVED, upon presentment of an itemized statement, that the Treasurer of

This Corporation is directed to reimburse                         , for moneys

advanced and expenses incurred and paid for by

in connection with the business purposes of this Corporation.

     I certify that I am the duly elected and qualified Secretary and that the above is a

true and correct copy of a resolution duly adopted at a meeting of the Board of Directors

thereof, convened and held in accordance with the law and the By-laws of said

Corporation on               , 19    , and that such resolution is now in full

force and effect.

     IN WITNESS WHEREOF, I have affixed my name as secretary and have

caused the corporate seal of said Corporation to be hereunto affixed this

day of          , 19    .


A True Record

Attest

                              _____

                                    Secretary

# RESOLUTION OF BOARD OF DIRECTORS OF

_____

WHEREAS, this Corporation, has undistributed surplus of

Dollars ($                ), and

WHEREAS, the Board of Directors has decided that

Dollars ($                ) should be set aside from the undistributed surplus funds for the

purpose of declaring a stock dividend to be distributed to the holders of outstanding

common shares of the Corporation; be it

RESOLVED, That a stock dividend is declared in the amount of

per share of the common stock of this Corporation and that the same

shall be paid by the Treasurer on                          , 19      , to

shareholders of record as of                    , 19      .

FURTHER, RESOLVED, That the Treasurer is directed to transfer

Dollars ($                ) from surplus to the capital account.

I certify that I am the duly elected and qualified Secretary and that the above is a

true and correct copy of a resolution duly adopted at a meeting of the Board of Directors

thereof, convened and held in accordance with the law and the By-laws of said

Corporation on                          , 19      , and that such resolution is now in full

force and effect.

IN WITNESS WHEREOF, I have affixed my name as secretary and have

caused the corporate seal of said Corporation to be hereunto affixed this

day of                    , 19      .

A True Record

Attest

_____

Secretary

# RESOLUTION OF BOARD OF DIRECTORS OF

_____

      RESOLVED, That the dividend policy of the Company is to place the capital stock of the Company on a dividend basis of $           per annum, payable on the first day of          , subject to the specific declaration and determination of the said dividends payable from time to time by the Board of Directors.

      I certify that I am the duly elected and qualified Secretary and that the above is a true and correct copy of a resolution duly adopted at a meeting of the Board of Directors thereof, convened and held in accordance with the law and the By-laws of said Corporation on          , 19    , and that such resolution is now in full force and effect.

      IN WITNESS WHEREOF, I have affixed my name as secretary and have caused the corporate seal of said Corporation to be hereunto affixed this day of          , 19    .


A True Record

Attest

                                       _____

                                            Secretary

# RESOLUTION OF BOARD OF DIRECTORS OF

RESOLVED, That the quarterly dividend of this Corporation be declared

payable to holders of record as of                , 19      , of the common

stock of this Corporation, in the amount of             per share of stock, and

the Treasurer shall pay same on              , 19   .

I certify that I am the duly elected and qualified Secretary and that the above is a

true and correct copy of a resolution duly adopted at a meeting of the Board of Directors

thereof, convened and held in accordance with the law and the By-laws of said

Corporation on              , 19     , and that such resolution is now in full

force and effect.

IN WITNESS WHEREOF, I have affixed my name as secretary and have

caused the corporate seal of said Corporation to be hereunto affixed this

day of             , 19    .


A True Record

Attest

_____
                 Secretary

# RESOLUTION OF BOARD OF DIRECTORS OF

_____

WHEREAS, The directors desire to improve the financial condition of the

Company, be it

RESOLVED, That no dividends be declared for fiscal year 19     , and that any

earnings of the Company for the year 19        be credited to the Surplus Account.

I certify that I am the duly elected and qualified Secretary and that the above is a

true and correct copy of a resolution duly adopted at a meeting of the Board of Directors

thereof, convened and held in accordance with the law and the By-laws of said

Corporation on                            , 19      , and that such resolution is now in full

force and effect.

IN WITNESS WHEREOF, I have affixed my name as secretary and have

caused the corporate seal of said Corporation to be hereunto affixed this

day of                   , 19       .


A True Record

Attest

_____

Secretary

# RESOLUTION OF BOARD OF DIRECTORS OF

_____

RESOLVED, That the officers of this Corporation be obligated to repay to the Corporation that sum paid to such officers as salary or expenses that is disallowed by the Internal Revenue Service as a deduction in the computation of the Corporation's federal income tax.

I certify that I am the duly elected and qualified Secretary and that the above is a true and correct copy of a resolution duly adopted at a meeting of the Board of Directors thereof, convened and held in accordance with the law and the By-laws of said Corporation on                              , 19       , and that such resolution is now in full force and effect.

IN WITNESS WHEREOF, I have affixed my name as secretary and have caused the corporate seal of said Corporation to be hereunto affixed this day of                    , 19       .

A True Record

Attest

                                         _____

                                         Secretary

# CERTIFICATE OF CONSENT OF

_____

We, the undersigned officers, agree to repay to the Corporation that part of our salary or expenses granted for 19      that has been disallowed as a deduction in the computation of the Corporation's federal income tax for 19      . We further agree to make any such repayment within 90 days after final disallowance of the aforesaid deduction by the Internal Revenue Service (or any court to which the Corporation may appeal).

| Name | Title | Signature |
| --- | --- | --- |
| _____ | _____ | _____ |
| _____ | _____ | _____ |
| _____ | _____ | _____ |
| _____ | _____ | _____ |

I certify that I am the duly elected and qualified Secretary and that the above is a true and correct copy of a resolution duly adopted at a meeting of the Board of Directors thereof, convened and held in accordance with the law and the By-laws of said Corporation on                      , 19      , and that such resolution is now in full force and effect.

IN WITNESS WHEREOF, I have affixed my name as secretary and have caused the corporate seal of said Corporation to be hereunto affixed this

day of                   , 19      .

A True Record

Attest

_____

Secretary

# Resolutions on Employee Benefits

# RESOLUTION OF BOARD OF DIRECTORS OF

_____

WHEREAS, The Board of Directors believes that a profit-sharing plan will encourage greater productivity, be it

RESOLVED, That an Employee Profit-Sharing Plan, a copy of which is hereby annexed to and made a part of the minutes of this meeting, is hereby adopted, subject to the approval of the stockholders at their special meeting to be called after a favorable ruling under Secs. 401(a) and 404 of the Internal Revenue Code of 1954 has been obtained from the Internal Revenue Service.

RESOLVED, FURTHER, That                                                    ,

Secretary of this Corporation, is directed on behalf of this Corporation to execute and deliver the Trust Agreement between                                        and

                            , Trustee, pursuant to

Profit-Sharing Plan, a copy being annexed to and made part of the minutes of this meeting, and

RESOLVED, FURTHER, That                                                    ,

                                , and                                        are

appointed members of, and shall constitute, the Profit-Sharing Committee provided for in                                        Profit-Sharing Plan and shall hold office until the next annual meeting of the Board of Directors or until their successors are duly appointed, and

RESOLVED, FURTHER, That the President is authorized to retain

                            as counsel and to instruct counsel to take such action as necessary to secure a ruling from the Internal Revenue Service that

                            Employee Profit-Sharing Plan is qualified under Secs 401(a) and

404 of the Internal Revenue Code of 1954 and to take such other action as necessary, and counsel shall thereupon provide the Board his opinion as to full legal compliance.

I certify that I am the duly elected and qualified Secretary and that the above is a true and correct copy of a resolution duly adopted at a meeting of the Board of Directors thereof, convened and held in accordance with the law and the By-laws of said Corporation on                              , 19     , and that such resolution is now in full force and effect.

IN WITNESS WHEREOF, I have affixed my name as secretary and have caused the corporate seal of said Corporation to be hereunto affixed this

day of                    , 19      .


A True Record

Attest

_____

Secretary

# RESOLUTION OF BOARD OF DIRECTORS OF

_____

WHEREAS, the Board of Directors of this Corporation considers it advisable to provide for the retirement security of its employees, be it

RESOLVED, That the Pension Plan (a copy being annexed to the minutes of this meeting and made a permanent part thereof) be hereby adopted.

I certify that I am the duly elected and qualified Secretary, and this is a true and correct copy of a resolution duly adopted at a meeting of the Board of Directors thereof, legally convened and held in accordance with the By-laws of said Corporation on

            , 19      , and that this resolution is presently in full force and effect.

IN WITNESS WHEREOF, I have affixed my name as Secretary and have imprinted the corporate seal this              day of              , 19      .


A True Record

Attest

                                        _____

                                                    Secretary

# RESOLUTION OF BOARD OF DIRECTORS OF

_____

WHEREAS, the Stockholders of this Corporation have approved the Stock

Option Plan and have authorized the Board of Directors to give certain employees the

option to buy shares under the provisions of said plan and to allocate

(                    ) shares of the common stock, without par value, of this Corporation for

said purpose, be it

RESOLVED, That the Board of Directors hereby allocates a total of

(                    ) shares of the common stock, without par value, for

sale to said employees under the terms of said Stock Option Plan.

I certify that I am the duly elected and qualified Secretary, and this is a true and

correct copy of a resolution duly adopted at a meeting of the Board of Directors thereof,

legally convened and held in accordance with the By-laws of said Corporation on

, 19      , and that such resolution is now in full force and effect.

IN WITNESS WHEREOF, I have affixed my name as Secretary and have

imprinted the corporate seal this                    day of                    , 19      .


A True Record

Attest

_____

Secretary

# RESOLUTION OF BOARD OF DIRECTORS OF

WHEREAS, a health care program is desirable to encourage company-employee relations, be it

RESOLVED, That the Employee Medical-Dental Expense Plan (a copy of which is annexed to the minutes of this meeting) is approved and adopted.

I certify that I am the duly elected and qualified Secretary and that the above is a true and correct copy of a resolution duly adopted at a meeting of the Board of Directors thereof, convened and held in accordance with law and the By-laws of said Corporation on                              , 19      , and that such resolution is now in full force and effect.

IN WITNESS WHEREOF, I have affixed my name as Secretary and have caused the corporate seal of said Corporation to be hereunto affixed this day of                     , 19      .


A True Record

Attest

_____
                                      Secretary

# RESOLUTION OF BOARD OF DIRECTORS OF

_____

WHEREAS, this Corporation has considered a plan granting wage payments to sick and injured employees, and

WHEREAS, the officers have presented to this meeting their recommendation for the adoption of a Wage Continuation Plan (a copy of which is attached) be it

RESOLVED, That the Board of Directors adopts the annexed Wage Continuation Plan and that the Treasurer of this Corporation is directed to make payments to eligible employees in accordance with said Plan.

I certify that I am the duly elected and qualified Secretary and that the above is a true and correct copy of a resolution duly adopted at a meeting of the Board of Directors thereof, convened and held in accordance with law and the By-laws of said Corporation on                          , 19      , and that such resolution is now in full force and effect.

IN WITNESS WHEREOF, I have affixed my name as Secretary and have caused the corporate seal of said Corporation to be hereunto affixed this day of                   , 19      .


A True Record

Attest

_____

Secretary

# RESOLUTION OF BOARD OF DIRECTORS OF

_____

WHEREAS, a group legal services plan is desirable to promote better company-employee relations by making low-cost legal services available to employees, be it

RESOLVED, That the Treasurer be authorized to contract with

, for a group legal services plan as annexed.

I certify that I am the duly elected and qualified Secretary and that the above is a true and correct copy of a resolution duly adopted at a meeting of the Board of Directors thereof, convened and held in accordance with law and the By-laws of said Corporation on                                    , 19      , and that such resolution is now in full force and effect.

IN WITNESS WHEREOF, I have affixed my name as Secretary and have caused the corporate seal of said Corporation to be hereunto affixed this day of                      , 19      .


A True Record

Attest

_____

Secretary

# RESOLUTION OF BOARD OF DIRECTORS OF

_____

WHEREAS, a group insurance program is desirable to promote better company-employee relations by providing career employees with no-cost life insurance, be it

RESOLVED, That the Treasurer is authorized to contract for a group insurance program, as annexed.

I certify that I am the duly elected and qualified Secretary and that the above is a true and correct copy of a resolution duly adopted at a meeting of the Board of Directors thereof, convened and held in accordance with law and the By-laws of said Corporation on                          , 19     , and that such resolution is now in full force and effect.

IN WITNESS WHEREOF, I have affixed my name as Secretary and have caused the corporate seal of said Corporation to be hereunto affixed this day of                 , 19     .


A True Record

Attest

                                        _____

                                        Secretary

# RESOLUTION OF DIRECTORS OF

_____

RESOLVED, Upon recommendation of the Board, the Employee Benefit Plan appended to this resolution is hereby approved, and,

RESOLVED, FURTHER, That the Board of Directors is hereby authorized to set aside from profits such sums as they deem proper but not to exceed             percent (      %) of said net profits, for the purpose of funding such benefit plan.

I certify that I am the duly elected and qualified Secretary and that the above is a true and correct copy of a resolution duly adopted at a meeting of the Board of Directors thereof, convened and held in accordance with law and the By-laws of said Corporation on                          , 19      , and that such resolution is now in full force and effect.

IN WITNESS WHEREOF, I have affixed my name as Secretary and have caused the corporate seal of said Corporation to be hereunto affixed this

day of                   , 19      .


A True Record

Attest

_____

Secretary

# RESOLUTION OF DIRECTORS OF

---

WHEREAS, the officers of the Corporation have prepared and submitted to the Board of Directors an Employees' Welfare Plan, a copy of which is hereto annexed, be it

RESOLVED, That the Board of Directors hereby adopts the Employees' Welfare Plan as set forth in the annexed copy, subject to the approval of the stockholders at their next meeting, and

RESOLVED, FURTHER, That the officers of the Corporation are hereby authorized to take such action as may be necessary to implement the Plan.

I certify that I am the duly elected and qualified Secretary and that the above is a true and correct copy of a resolution duly adopted at a meeting of the Board of Directors thereof, convened and held in accordance with law and the By-laws of said Corporation on                              , 19      , and that such resolution is now in full force and effect.

IN WITNESS WHEREOF, I have affixed my name as Secretary and have caused the corporate seal of said Corporation to be hereunto affixed this day of                   , 19      .


A True Record

Attest

_____
Secretary

# RESOLUTION OF BOARD OF DIRECTORS OF

_____

RESOLVED, That the President of the Corporation is authorized to contract with

Insurance Company, under which

contract the Corporation shall, on the death of                                                    ,

pay the sum of                    Dollars ($                    ) to the beneficiary or

beneficiaries named in the above contract, provided that

is still in the employment of the Corporation at the time of his death or shall have retired

under the Corporation's retirement policy.

I certify that I am the duly elected and qualified Secretary and that the above is a

true and correct copy of a resolution duly adopted at a meeting of the Board of Directors

thereof, convened and held in accordance with law and the By-laws of said Corporation

on                                  , 19       , and that such resolution is now in full force

and effect.

IN WITNESS WHEREOF, I have affixed my name as Secretary and have

caused the corporate seal of said Corporation to be hereunto affixed this

day of                       , 19          .


A True Record

Attest

_____

Secretary

# RESOLUTION OF BOARD OF DIRECTORS OF

_____

WHEREAS,                          , a

of this Corporation has requested a loan from the Corporation in the sum of

                    Dollars ($          ), and has offered

                   as security for said loan, and has agreed to pay interest

on said loan at the rate of              per cent (     %) per annum, and

      WHEREAS, the said Corporation has sufficient surplus funds to advance the

said sum of                   Dollars ($        ), be it

      RESOLVED, That                     , the President, and

           , the Treasurer of this Corporation, are hereby

authorized to issue a loan to the said               for the sum of

           Dollars ($        ) upon receipt by them

of said security.

      I certify that I am the duly elected and qualified Secretary and that the above is a

true and correct copy of a resolution duly adopted at a meeting of the Board of Directors

thereof, convened and held in accordance with law and the By-laws of said Corporation

on                , 19    , and that such resolution is now in full force

and effect.

      IN WITNESS WHEREOF, I have affixed my name as Secretary and have

caused the corporate seal of said Corporation to be hereunto affixed this

day of           , 19    .

A True Record

Attest

                               _____

                                    Secretary

# Miscellaneous Corporate Documents

# STOCK TRANSFER LEDGER

| NAME OF STOCKHOLDER | PLACE OF RESIDENCE | | CERTIFICATES ISSUED | | FROM WHOM SHARES WERE TRANSFERRED (IF ORIGINAL ISSUE ENTER AS SUCH) | |
| | | | CERTIF. NOS. | NO. SHARES | | |
| --- | --- | --- | --- | --- | --- | --- |
| | | | | | | |
| | | | | | | |
| | | | | | | |
| | | | | | | |
| | | | | | | |
| | | | | | | |
| | | | | | | |
| | | | | | | |
| | | | | | | |
| | | | | | | |
| | | | | | | |
| | | | | | | |
| | | | | | | |
| | | | | | | |
| | | | | | | |
| | | | | | | |
| | | | | | | |
| | | | | | | |
| | | | | | | |
| | | | | | | |
| | | | | | | |
| | | | | | | |
| | | | | | | |
| | | | | | | |
| | | | | | | |
| | | | | | | |
| | | | | | | |
| | | | | | | |
| | | | | | | |
| | | | | | | |
| | | | | | | |
| | | | | | | |
| | | | | | | |
| | | | | | | |
| | | | | | | |
| | | | | | | |
| | | | | | | |

| AMOUNT PAID THEREON | DATE OF TRANSFER OF SHARES | TO WHOM SHARES ARE TRANSFERRED | CERTIFICATES SURRENDERED | | NUMBER OF SHARES HELD (BALANCE) | VALUE OF STOCK TRANSFER TAX STAMP AFFIXED | |
|---|---|---|---|---|---|---|---|
| | | | CERTIF. NOS. | NO. SHARES | | | |
| | | | | | | | |
| | | | | | | | |
| | | | | | | | |
| | | | | | | | |
| | | | | | | | |
| | | | | | | | |
| | | | | | | | |
| | | | | | | | |
| | | | | | | | |
| | | | | | | | |
| | | | | | | | |
| | | | | | | | |
| | | | | | | | |
| | | | | | | | |
| | | | | | | | |
| | | | | | | | |
| | | | | | | | |
| | | | | | | | |
| | | | | | | | |
| | | | | | | | |
| | | | | | | | |
| | | | | | | | |
| | | | | | | | |
| | | | | | | | |
| | | | | | | | |
| | | | | | | | |
| | | | | | | | |
| | | | | | | | |
| | | | | | | | |
| | | | | | | | |
| | | | | | | | |

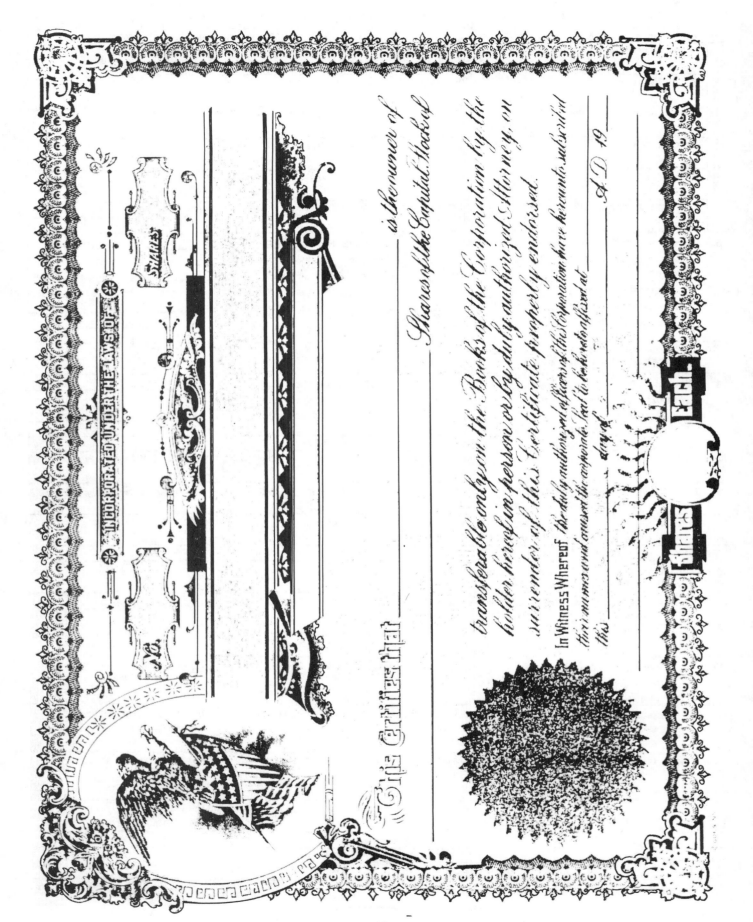

INCORPORATED UNDER THE LAWS OF

SHARES

No.

This Certifies that

is the owner of

Shares of the Capital Stock of

transferable only upon the Books of the Corporation by the
holder hereof in person or by duly authorized Attorney, on
surrender of this Certificate properly endorsed.

In Witness Whereof the duly authorized officers of the Corporation have hereunto subscribed
their names and caused the corporate Seal to be hereto affixed at
this                    day of                                        A. D. 19

Shares                    Each.

# Form SS-4
(Rev. December 1993)

Department of the Treasury
Internal Revenue Service

# Application for Employer Identification Number

(For use by employers, corporations, partnerships, trusts, estates, churches, government agencies, certain individuals, and others. See instructions.)

EIN

OMB No. 1545-0003
Expires 12-31-96

*Please type or print clearly.*

**1** Name of applicant (Legal name) (See instructions.)

**2** Trade name of business, if different from name in line 1

**3** Executor, trustee, "care of" name

**4a** Mailing address (street address) (room, apt., or suite no.)

**5a** Business address, if different from address in lines 4a and 4b

**4b** City, state, and ZIP code

**5b** City, state, and ZIP code

**6** County and state where principal business is located

**7** Name of principal officer, general partner, grantor, owner, or trustor—SSN required (See instructions.) ▶

**8a** Type of entity (Check only one box.) (See instructions.)

☐ Sole Proprietor (SSN) _____
☐ REMIC          ☐ Personal service corp.
☐ State/local government   ☐ National guard
☐ Other nonprofit organization (specify) _____
☐ Other (specify) ▶ _____

☐ Estate (SSN of decedent) _____
☐ Plan administrator-SSN _____
☐ Other corporation (specify) _____
☐ Federal government/military   ☐ Church or church controlled organization
(enter GEN if applicable) _____

☐ Trust
☐ Partnership
☐ Farmers' cooperative

**8b** If a corporation, name the state or foreign country (if applicable) where incorporated ▶

State

Foreign country

**9** Reason for applying (Check only one box.)

☐ Started new business (specify) ▶ _____
☐ Hired employees
☐ Created a pension plan (specify type) ▶ _____
☐ Banking purpose (specify) ▶ _____

☐ Changed type of organization (specify) ▶ _____
☐ Purchased going business
☐ Created a trust (specify) ▶ _____
☐ Other (specify) ▶ _____

**10** Date business started or acquired (Mo., day, year) (See instructions.)

**11** Enter closing month of accounting year. (See instructions.)

**12** First date wages or annuities were paid or will be paid (Mo., day, year). **Note:** *If applicant is a withholding agent, enter date income will first be paid to nonresident alien. (Mo., day, year)* . . . . . . . . . . . . . . . . ▶

**13** Enter highest number of employees expected in the next 12 months. **Note:** *If the applicant does not expect to have any employees during the period, enter "0."* . . . . . . . ▶

| Nonagricultural | Agricultural | Household |
|---|---|---|
| | | |

**14** Principal activity (See instructions.) ▶

**15** Is the principal business activity manufacturing? . . . . . . . . . . . . . . . ☐ Yes   ☐ No
If "Yes," principal product and raw material used ▶

**16** To whom are most of the products or services sold? Please check the appropriate box.   ☐ Business (wholesale)
☐ Public (retail)      ☐ Other (specify) ▶                                  ☐ N/A

**17a** Has the applicant ever applied for an identification number for this or any other business? . . . . . . . . ☐ Yes   ☐ No
**Note:** *If "Yes," please complete lines 17b and 17c.*

**17b** If you checked the "Yes" box in line 17a, give applicant's legal name and trade name, if different than name shown on prior application.

Legal name ▶                    Trade name ▶

**17c** Enter approximate date, city, and state where the application was filed and the previous employer identification number if known.

| Approximate date when filed (Mo., day, year) | City and state where filed | Previous EIN |
|---|---|---|
| | | |

Under penalties of perjury, I declare that I have examined this application, and to the best of my knowledge and belief, it is true, correct, and complete.

Business telephone number (include area code)

Name and title (Please type or print clearly.) ▶

Signature ▶                                                Date ▶

**Note:** *Do not write below this line.    For official use only.*

| Please leave blank ▶ | Geo. | Ind. | Class | Size | Reason for applying |
|---|---|---|---|---|---|
| | | | | | |

For Paperwork Reduction Act Notice, see attached instructions.

Cat. No. 16055N

Form **SS-4** (Rev. 12-93)

Form **2553**

(Rev. September 1993)

Department of the Treasury
Internal Revenue Service

# Election by a Small Business Corporation
### (Under section 1362 of the Internal Revenue Code)
▶ For Paperwork Reduction Act Notice, see page 1 of instructions.
▶ See separate instructions.

OMB No. 1545-0146
Expires 8-31-96

**Notes:** 1. *This election, to be an "S corporation," can be accepted only if all the tests are met under **Who May Elect** on page 1 of the instructions; all signatures in Parts I and III are originals (no photocopies); and the exact name and address of the corporation and other required form information are provided.*

2. *Do not file **Form 1120S**, U.S. Income Tax Return for an S Corporation, until you are notified that your election is accepted.*

| Part I | Election Information |
|---|---|

**Please Type or Print**

| | |
|---|---|
| Name of corporation (see instructions) | **A** Employer identification number (EIN) |
| Number, street, and room or suite no. (If a P.O. box, see instructions.) | **B** Date incorporated |
| City or town, state, and ZIP code | **C** State of incorporation |

**D** Election is to be effective for tax year beginning (month, day, year) . . . . . . . . . . . . . . . ▶    /    /

**E** Name and title of officer or legal representative who the IRS may call for more information

**F** Telephone number of officer or legal representative
(    )

**G** If the corporation changed its name or address after applying for the EIN shown in **A**, check this box . . . . . . . . . ▶ ☐

**H** If this election takes effect for the first tax year the corporation exists, enter month, day, and year of the **earliest** of the following: (1) date the corporation first had shareholders, (2) date the corporation first had assets, or (3) date the corporation began doing business . . . . . . . . . . . . . . . . . ▶    /    /

**I** Selected tax year: Annual return will be filed for tax year ending (month and day) ▶ ...............................

If the tax year ends on any date other than December 31, except for an automatic 52-53-week tax year ending with reference to the month of December, you **must** complete Part II on the back. If the date you enter is the ending date of an automatic 52-53-week tax year, write "52-53-week year" to the right of the date. See Temporary Regulations section 1.441-2T(e)(3).

| J Name and address of each shareholder, shareholder's spouse having a community property interest in the corporation's stock, and each tenant in common, joint tenant, and tenant by the entirety. (A husband and wife (and their estates) are counted as one shareholder in determining the number of shareholders without regard to the manner in which the stock is owned.) | K Shareholders' Consent Statement. Under penalties of perjury, we declare that we consent to the election of the above-named corporation to be an "S corporation" under section 1362(a) and that we have examined this consent statement, including accompanying schedules and statements, and to the best of our knowledge and belief, it is true, correct, and complete. (Shareholders sign and date below.)* | | L Stock owned | | M Social security number or employer identification number (see instructions) | N Share-holder's tax year ends (month and day) |
|---|---|---|---|---|---|---|
| | Signature | Date | Number of shares | Dates acquired | | |
| | | | | | | |
| | | | | | | |
| | | | | | | |
| | | | | | | |
| | | | | | | |

*For this election to be valid, the consent of each shareholder, shareholder's spouse having a community property interest in the corporation's stock, and each tenant in common, joint tenant, and tenant by the entirety must either appear above or be attached to this form. (See instructions for Column K if a continuation sheet or a separate consent statement is needed.)

Under penalties of perjury, I declare that I have examined this election, including accompanying schedules and statements, and to the best of my knowledge and belief, it is true, correct, and complete.

Signature of officer ▶                     Title ▶                     Date ▶

**See Parts II and III on back.**              Cat. No. 18629R              Form **2553** (Rev. 9-93)

L 97

**Part II**  **Selection of Fiscal Tax Year (All corporations using this part must complete item O and one of items P, Q, or R.)**

**O**  Check the applicable box below to indicate whether the corporation is:

1. ☐ A new corporation adopting the tax year entered in item I, Part I.

2. ☐ An existing corporation retaining the tax year entered in item I, Part I.

3. ☐ An existing corporation changing to the tax year entered in item I, Part I.

**P**  Complete item P if the corporation is using the expeditious approval provisions of Revenue Procedure 87-32, 1987-2 C.B. 396, to request: **(1)** a natural business year (as defined in section 4.01(1) of Rev. Proc. 87-32), or **(2)** a year that satisfies the ownership tax year test in section 4.01(2) of Rev. Proc. 87-32. Check the applicable box below to indicate the representation statement the corporation is making as required under section 4 of Rev. Proc. 87-32.

**1. Natural Business Year ►** ☐ I represent that the corporation is retaining or changing to a tax year that coincides with its natural business year as defined in section 4.01(1) of Rev. Proc. 87-32 and as verified by its satisfaction of the requirements of section 4.02(1) of Rev. Proc. 87-32. In addition, if the corporation is changing to a natural business year as defined in section 4.01(1), I further represent that such tax year results in less deferral of income to the owners than the corporation's present tax year. I also represent that the corporation is not described in section 3.01(2) of Rev. Proc. 87-32. (See instructions for additional information that must be attached.)

**2. Ownership Tax Year ►** ☐ I represent that shareholders holding more than half of the shares of the stock (as of the first day of the tax year to which the request relates) of the corporation have the same tax year or are concurrently changing to the tax year that the corporation adopts, retains, or changes to per item I, Part I. I also represent that the corporation is not described in section 3.01(2) of Rev. Proc. 87-32.

**Note:** *If you do not use item P and the corporation wants a fiscal tax year, complete either item Q or R below. Item Q is used to request a fiscal tax year based on a business purpose and to make a back-up section 444 election. Item R is used to make a regular section 444 election.*

**Q**  Business Purpose—To request a fiscal tax year based on a business purpose, you must check box Q1 and pay a user fee. See instructions for details. You may also check box Q2 and/or box Q3.

**1. Check here ►** ☐ if the fiscal year entered in item I, Part I, is requested under the provisions of section 6.03 of Rev. Proc. 87-32. Attach to Form 2553 a statement showing the business purpose for the requested fiscal year. See instructions for additional information that must be attached.

**2. Check here ►** ☐ to show that the corporation intends to make a back-up section 444 election in the event the corporation's business purpose request is not approved by the IRS. (See instructions for more information.)

**3. Check here ►** ☐ to show that the corporation agrees to adopt or change to a tax year ending December 31 if necessary for the IRS to accept this election for S corporation status in the event: (1) the corporation's business purpose request is not approved and the corporation makes a back-up section 444 election, but is ultimately not qualified to make a section 444 election, or (2) the corporation's business purpose request is not approved and the corporation did not make a back-up section 444 election.

**R**  Section 444 Election—To make a section 444 election, you must check box R1 and you may also check box R2.

**1. Check here ►** ☐ to show the corporation will make, if qualified, a section 444 election to have the fiscal tax year shown in item I, Part I. To make the election, you must complete **Form 8716**, Election To Have a Tax Year Other Than a Required Tax Year, and either attach it to Form 2553 or file it separately.

**2. Check here ►** ☐ to show that the corporation agrees to adopt or change to a tax year ending December 31 if necessary for the IRS to accept this election for S corporation status in the event the corporation is ultimately not qualified to make a section 444 election.

**Part III**  **Qualified Subchapter S Trust (QSST) Election Under Section 1361(d)(2)\*\***

| Income beneficiary's name and address | Social security number |
|---|---|
| | |
| Trust's name and address | Employer identification number |
| | |

Date on which stock of the corporation was transferred to the trust (month, day, year) . . . . . . . . . ►     /     /

In order for the trust named above to be a QSST and thus a qualifying shareholder of the S corporation for which this Form 2553 is filed, I hereby make the election under section 1361(d)(2). Under penalties of perjury, I certify that the trust meets the definitional requirements of section 1361(d)(3) and that all other information provided in Part III is true, correct, and complete.

| Signature of income beneficiary or signature and title of legal representative or other qualified person making the election | Date |
|---|---|

\*\*Use of Part III to make the QSST election may be made only if stock of the corporation has been transferred to the trust on or before the date on which the corporation makes its election to be an S corporation. The QSST election must be made and filed separately if stock of the corporation is transferred to the trust after the date on which the corporation makes the S election.

## Department of the Treasury
### Internal Revenue Service

# Instructions for Form 2553
## (Revised September 1993)

### Election by a Small Business Corporation

*Section references are to the Internal Revenue Code unless otherwise noted.*

**Paperwork Reduction Act Notice.**—We ask for the information on this form to carry out the Internal Revenue laws of the United States. You are required to give us the information. We need it to ensure that you are complying with these laws and to allow us to figure and collect the right amount of tax.

The time needed to complete and file this form will vary depending on individual circumstances. The estimated average time is:

| | |
|---|---|
| **Recordkeeping** | 6 hr., 13 min. |
| **Learning about the law or the form** | 2 hr., 59 min. |
| **Preparing, copying, assembling, and sending the form to the IRS** | 3 hr., 13 min. |

If you have comments concerning the accuracy of these time estimates or suggestions for making this form more simple, we would be happy to hear from you. You can write to both the **Internal Revenue Service,** Attention: Reports Clearance Officer, T:FP, Washington, DC 20224; and the **Office of Management and Budget,** Paperwork Reduction Project (1545-0146), Washington, DC 20503. **DO NOT** send the tax form to either of these offices. Instead, see **Where To File** below.

## General Instructions

**Purpose.**—To elect to be an "S corporation," a corporation must file Form 2553. The election permits the income of the S corporation to be taxed to the shareholders of the corporation rather than to the corporation itself, except as provided in Subchapter S of the Code. For more information, get **Pub. 589,** Tax Information on S Corporations.

**Who May Elect.**—A corporation may elect to be an S corporation only if it meets **all** of the following tests:

1. It is a domestic corporation.

2. It has no more than 35 shareholders. A husband and wife (and their estates) are treated as one shareholder for this requirement. All other persons are treated as separate shareholders.

3. It has only individuals, estates, or certain trusts as shareholders. See the instructions for Part III regarding qualified subchapter S trusts.

4. It has no nonresident alien shareholders.

5. It has only one class of stock (disregarding differences in voting rights). Generally, a corporation is treated as having only one class of stock if all outstanding shares of the corporation's stock confer identical rights to distribution and liquidation

proceeds. See Regulations section 1.1361-1(l) for more details.

6. It is not one of the following ineligible corporations:

a. A corporation that owns 80% or more of the stock of another corporation, unless the other corporation has not begun business and has no gross income;

b. A bank or thrift institution;

c. An insurance company subject to tax under the special rules of Subchapter L of the Code;

d. A corporation that has elected to be treated as a possessions corporation under section 936; or

e. A domestic international sales corporation (DISC) or former DISC.

7. It has a permitted tax year as required by section 1378 or makes a section 444 election to have a tax year other than a permitted tax year. Section 1378 defines a permitted tax year as a tax year ending December 31, or any other tax year for which the corporation establishes a business purpose to the satisfaction of the IRS. See Part II for details on requesting a fiscal tax year based on a business purpose or on making a section 444 election.

8. Each shareholder consents as explained in the instructions for Column K.

See sections 1361, 1362, and 1378 for additional information on the above tests.

**Where To File.**—File this election with the Internal Revenue Service Center listed below.

| If the corporation's principal business, office, or agency is located in | Use the following Internal Revenue Service Center address |
|---|---|
| New Jersey, New York (New York City and counties of Nassau, Rockland, Suffolk, and Westchester) | Holtsville, NY 00501 |
| New York (all other counties), Connecticut, Maine, Massachusetts, New Hampshire, Rhode Island, Vermont | Andover, MA 05501 |
| Illinois, Iowa, Minnesota, Missouri, Wisconsin | Kansas City, MO 64999 |
| Delaware, District of Columbia, Maryland, Pennsylvania, Virginia | Philadelphia, PA 19255 |
| Florida, Georgia, South Carolina | Atlanta, GA 39901 |
| Indiana, Kentucky, Michigan, Ohio, West Virginia | Cincinnati, OH 45999 |
| Kansas, New Mexico, Oklahoma, Texas | Austin, TX 73301 |

| | |
|---|---|
| Alaska, Arizona, California (counties of Alpine, Amador, Butte, Calaveras, Colusa, Contra Costa, Del Norte, El Dorado, Glenn, Humboldt, Lake, Lassen, Marin, Mendocino, Modoc, Napa, Nevada, Placer, Plumas, Sacramento, San Joaquin, Shasta, Sierra, Siskiyou, Solano, Sonoma, Sutter, Tehama, Trinity, Yolo, and Yuba), Colorado, Idaho, Montana, Nebraska, Nevada, North Dakota, Oregon, South Dakota, Utah, Washington, Wyoming | Ogden, UT 84201 |
| California (all other counties), Hawaii | Fresno, CA 93888 |
| Alabama, Arkansas, Louisiana, Mississippi, North Carolina, Tennessee | Memphis, TN 37501 |

**When To Make the Election.**—Complete and file Form 2553 **(a)** at any time before the 16th day of the third month of the tax year, if filed during the tax year the election is to take effect, or **(b)** at any time during the preceding tax year. An election made no later than 2 months and 15 days after the beginning of a tax year that is less than 2½ months long is treated as timely made for that tax year. An election made after the 15th day of the third month but before the end of the tax year is effective for the next year. For example, if a calendar tax year corporation makes the election in April 1994, it is effective for the corporation's 1995 calendar tax year. See section 1362(b) for more information.

**Acceptance or Nonacceptance of Election.**—The Service Center will notify the corporation if its election is accepted and when it will take effect. The corporation will also be notified if its election is not accepted. The corporation should generally receive a determination on its election within 60 days after it has filed Form 2553. If box Q1 in Part II is checked on page 2, the corporation will receive a ruling letter from the IRS in Washington, DC, that either approves or denies the selected tax year. When box Q1 is checked, it will generally take an additional 90 days for the Form 2553 to be accepted.

Do not file Form 1120S until the corporation is notified that its election has been accepted. If the corporation is now required to file **Form 1120,** U.S. Corporation Income Tax Return, or any other applicable tax return, continue filing it until the election takes effect.

Care should be exercised to ensure that the IRS receives the election. If the corporation is not notified of acceptance or nonacceptance of its election within 3 months of date of filing (date mailed), or within 6 months if box Q1 is checked, please take follow-up action by corresponding with the Service Center where the corporation filed the election. If the IRS questions whether Form 2553 was filed, an acceptable proof of filing is: **(a)** certified or registered mail receipt (timely filed); **(b)** Form 2553 with accepted stamp; **(c)** Form 2553 with stamped IRS received date; or **(d)** IRS letter stating that Form 2553 has been accepted.

**End of Election.—** Once the election is made, it stays in effect for all years until it is terminated. During the 5 years after the election is terminated under section 1362(d), the corporation (or a successor corporation) can make another election on Form 2553 only with IRS consent. See Regulations section 1.1362-5 for more details.

## Specific Instructions

### Part I

**Part I must be completed by all corporations.**

**Name and Address of Corporation.—**Enter the true corporate name as set forth in the corporate charter or other legal document creating it. If the corporation's mailing address is the same as someone else's, such as a shareholder's, please enter "c/o" and this person's name following the name of the corporation. Include the suite, room, or other unit number after the street address. If the Post Office does not deliver to the street address and the corporation has a P.O. box, show the box number instead of the street address. If the corporation changed its name or address after applying for its EIN, be sure to check the box in item G of Part I.

**Item A. Employer Identification Number.—**If the corporation has applied for an employer identification number (EIN) but has not received it, enter "applied for." If the corporation does not have an EIN, it should apply for one on **Form SS-4**, Application for Employer Identification Number, available from most IRS and Social Security Administration offices.

**Item D. Effective Date of Election.—**Enter the beginning effective date (month, day, year) of the tax year requested for the S corporation. Generally, this will be the beginning date of the tax year for which the ending effective date is required to be shown in item I, Part I. For a new corporation (first year the corporation exists) it will generally be the date required to be shown in item H, Part I. The tax year of a new corporation starts on the date that it has shareholders, acquires assets, or begins doing business, whichever happens first. If the effective date for item D for a newly formed corporation is later than the date in item H, the corporation should file Form 1120 or Form 1120-A, for the tax period between these dates.

**Column K. Shareholders' Consent Statement.—**Each shareholder who owns (or is deemed to own) stock at the time the election is made must consent to the election. If the election is made during the corporation's tax year for which it first takes effect, any person who held stock at any time during the part of that year that occurs before the election is made, must consent to the election, even though the person may have sold or transferred his or her stock before the

election is made. Each shareholder consents by signing and dating in column K or signing and dating a separate consent statement described below.

An election made during the first 2½ months of the tax year is effective for the following tax year if any person who held stock in the corporation during the part of the tax year before the election was made, and who did not hold stock at the time the election was made, did not consent to the election.

If a husband and wife have a community interest in the stock or in the income from it, both must consent. Each tenant in common, joint tenant, and tenant by the entirety also must consent.

A minor's consent is made by the minor or the legal representative of the minor, or by a natural or adoptive parent of the minor if no legal representative has been appointed.

The consent of an estate is made by an executor or administrator.

If stock is owned by a trust that is a qualified shareholder, the deemed owner of the trust must consent. See section 1361(c)(2) for details regarding qualified trusts that may be shareholders and rules on determining who is the deemed owner of the trust.

**Continuation sheet or separate consent statement.—**If you need a continuation sheet or use a separate consent statement, attach it to Form 2553. The separate consent statement must contain the name, address, and employer identification number of the corporation and the shareholder information requested in columns J through N of Part I.

If you want, you may combine all the shareholders' consents in one statement.

**Column L.—**Enter the number of shares of stock each shareholder owns and the dates the stock was acquired. If the election is made during the corporation's tax year for which it first takes effect, do not list the shares of stock for those shareholders who sold or transferred all of their stock before the election was made. However, these shareholders must still consent to the election for it to be effective for the tax year.

**Column M.—**Enter the social security number of each shareholder who is an individual. Enter the employer identification number of each shareholder that is an estate or a qualified trust.

**Column N.—**Enter the month and day that each shareholder's tax year ends. If a shareholder is changing his or her tax year, enter the tax year the shareholder is changing to, and attach an explanation indicating the present tax year and the basis for the change (e.g., automatic revenue procedure or letter ruling request).

If the election is made during the corporation's tax year for which it first takes effect, you do not have to enter the tax year of any shareholder who sold or transferred all of his or her stock before the election was made.

**Signature.—**Form 2553 must be signed by the president, treasurer, assistant treasurer, chief accounting officer, or other corporate officer (such as tax officer) authorized to sign.

### Part II

Complete Part II if you selected a tax year ending on any date other than December 31

(other than a 52-53-week tax year ending with reference to the month of December).

**Box P1.—**Attach a statement showing separately for each month the amount of gross receipts for the most recent 47 months as required by section 4.03(3) of Revenue Procedure 87-32, 1987-2 C.B. 396. A corporation that does not have a 47-month period of gross receipts cannot establish a natural business year under section 4.01(1).

**Box Q1.—**For examples of an acceptable business purpose for requesting a fiscal tax year, see Revenue Ruling 87-57, 1987-2 C.B. 117.

In addition to a statement showing the business purpose for the requested fiscal year, you must attach the other information necessary to meet the ruling request requirements of Revenue Procedure 93-1, 1993-1 I.R.B. 10 (updated annually). Also attach a statement that shows separately the amount of gross receipts from sales or services (and inventory costs, if applicable) for each of the 36 months preceding the effective date of the election to be an S corporation. If the corporation has been in existence for fewer than 36 months, submit figures for the period of existence.

If you check box Q1, you must also pay a user fee of $200 (subject to change). Do not pay the fee when filing Form 2553. The Service Center will send Form 2553 to the IRS in Washington, DC, who, in turn, will notify the corporation that the fee is due. See Revenue Procedure 93-23, 1993-19 I.R.B. 6.

**Box Q2.—**If the corporation makes a back-up section 444 election for which it is qualified, then the election must be exercised in the event the business purpose request is not approved. Under certain circumstances, the tax year requested under the back-up section 444 election may be different than the tax year requested under business purpose. See **Form 8716**, Election To Have a Tax Year Other Than a Required Tax Year, for details on making a back-up section 444 election.

**Boxes Q2 and R2.—**If the corporation is not qualified to make the section 444 election after making the item Q2 back-up section 444 election or indicating its intention to make the election in item R1, and therefore it later files a calendar year return, it should write "Section 444 Election Not Made" in the top left corner of the 1st calendar year Form 1120S it files.

### Part III

Certain Qualified Subchapter S Trusts (QSSTs) may make the QSST election required by section 1361(d)(2) in Part III. Part III may be used to make the QSST election only if corporate stock has been transferred to the trust on or before the date on which the corporation makes its election to be an S corporation. However, a statement can be used in lieu of Part III to make the election.

**Note:** *Part III may be used only in conjunction with making the Part I election (i.e., Form 2553 cannot be filed with only Part III completed).*

The deemed owner of the QSST must also consent to the S corporation election in column K, page 1, of Form 2553. See section 1361(c)(2).

# ASSIGNMENT OF ASSETS

This agreement is made and entered into this       day of

    , 19    , between

(Stockholder) and                           (Corporation).

WITNESSETH:

WHEREAS, on the        day of        , 19    , the Corporation was formed by Articles of Incorporation filed with the Secretary of State of        , and it is necessary to transfer assets to the Corporation to properly capitalize the Corporation; and

WHEREAS, Stockholder is desirous of transferring to the Corporation certain assets shown on the attached Exhibit "A," and the Corporation is desirous of acquiring said assets.

NOW, THEREFORE, for and in consideration of the agreements hereinafter entered into, it is agreed that:

1.     Stockholder shall transfer and assign those assets listed on the attached Exhibit "A" to the Corporation.

2.     In consideration for said transfer, the Corporation shall issue to Stockholder (      ) shares of       stock in the Corporation, par value $      per share.

DATED this      day of      , 19  .

_____

Stockholder


By: _____

Corporation

# Organizational Meetings and By-Laws

# NOTICE OF ORGANIZATION MEETING OF
# INCORPORATORS AND DIRECTORS

TO:

BE IT KNOWN THAT, we, a majority of the directors named in the Articles of

Incorporation of                                    (Corporate Name) , a

                    corporation (State of Incorporation), hereby call an organization

meeting of the Board of Directors and incorporators of

(Corporate Name). The purpose of said meeting is to adopt by-laws, elect officers, and

transact such other business as may come before the meeting; and

We hereby give notice that the organization meeting shall be on

, 19    , at        o'clock, held at the following address:

RECEIPT OF NOTICE

_____          _____

Addressee-Director                                    Date Received

# WAIVER OF ORGANIZATION MEETING OF
# INCORPORATORS AND DIRECTORS

BE IT KNOWN THAT, we, the incorporators and directors of

(Corporate Name) hereby agree to waive notice of the

organization meeting of directors and incorporators of the above-named corporation.

We hereby give notice that the organization meeting is rescheduled for

, 19    , at        o'clock, to be held at the following address:

All incorporators and directors must sign and date below:

_____          _____

(Signature)                          (Date)

_____          _____

_____          _____

_____          _____

_____          _____

_____          _____

# MINUTES, FIRST MEETING
# OF SHAREHOLDERS

---

BE IT KNOWN THAT the first meeting of the shareholders of

(Corporate Name) was held on                          , 19     ,

at        o'clock, at the following address:



                              , the President, duly called and held the meeting, the purpose of

which was the following:



The list of shareholders was read by                          , the Secretary, as they appear in

the Corporation's records. The Secretary affirmed and duly noted that the required

quorum of shareholders was present. The Secretary, as directed by the President, read the

minutes of the organization meeting of the Corporation and the minutes of the first

meeting of the Board of Directors.

Upon a motion, the following resolution was adopted:

BE IT RESOLVED that the election of the said directors and officers of

                              (Corporate Name) for the term of                          years

and said by-laws of the Corporation are ratified. That all acts taken at the organization

meeting and at the first meeting of the Board are approved and ratified, and that signing

of these minutes constitutes full ratification and waiver of notice of the meeting by the

signatories.

As all business had been completed, it was voted to adjourn on this

day of                              , 19    .

_____                    _____
(Secretary Signature)                              (Date)

_____                    _____
(Director Signature)                               (Date)

_____                    _____

_____                    _____

_____                    _____

# MINUTES OF ORGANIZATION MEETING
# OF BOARD OF DIRECTORS OF

_____

The organizational meeting of the Board of Directors of

(Corporate Name) on                                     , 19      , at

o'clock was held at the following premises:




The following Directors, designated in the Articles of Incorporation were present:




BE IT KNOWN THAT                                     acted as temporary Chairman

of the meeting and                          acted as temporary Secretary.

The Chairman announced that the meeting had been duly called by the

Incorporators of the Corporation, and reported that the Articles of Incorporation of the

(Corporate Name) had been duly filed with the State of

on                          , 19     . As part of the records of the

meeting, the Certificate of Incorporation and a copy of said Articles of Incorporation

were ordered inserted in the Minutes. Next was presented a proposed form of By-laws

for the regulation and the management of the affairs of

(Corporate Name). The By-laws were read and considered, and upon motion duly made

and seconded, it was RESOLVED THAT:

1) The form of By-laws of                          (Corporate Name) as

presented to this meeting, a copy of which is directed to be inserted in the Minutes Book

of the Corporation, is hereby approved and adopted as the By-laws of the Corporation.

2) The following persons were nominated officers of the Corporation to serve

until their respective successors are chosen and qualify:

PRESIDENT

VICE PRESIDENT

SECRETARY

TREASURER

Next, the President stated that several organizational matters had to be

considered at the meeting and a number of resolutions had to be adopted by the Board of

Directors, which include the following:

Upon motion duly made, seconded, and unanimously carried, the following

resolution was adopted:  RESOLVED, that, if required, that

(Name) be, and hereby is, appointed Resident Agent in the State of

The Resident Agent's office is located at the following premises:

_____

(Secretary's Signature)

_____

(Date)

# Annual and Special Meetings

# NOTICE TO SHAREHOLDERS
## OF ANNUAL MEETING

Notice is hereby given that the Annual Meeting of Shareholders of

for the purpose of electing a Board of

Directors for the ensuing year and transacting such other business as may properly come

before the meeting shall be held on the                day of

, 19        , at              o'clock    .m., at

, City of                                and State of              .

Transfer books shall remain closed from the                  day of

, 19       , until the                  day of                  ,

19     .


Dated the                    day of                  , 19      .



By Order of the Board of Directors


_____

Secretary

# MINUTES, SHAREHOLDERS'
# ANNUAL MEETING

The Annual Meeting of Shareholders of

was duly called and was held at                                                    ,

State of                              , on the                              day of

, 19    , at          o'clock,      .m.

The President called the meeting to order.

The Secretary next announced that a notice of meeting had been properly served, introducing an affidavit (or waiver) to this effect which was ordered placed on file.

The President proposed the election of a Chairman. A motion to that effect was duly made and carried.

It being determined that a quorum was present either in person or by proxy, a voice vote of shareholders was taken.                              was elected Chairman of the meeting.

A motion was duly made and carried that the Secretary read the minutes of the preceding meeting of shareholders. Upon completion of the reading, a motion was duly made and carried that the minutes be approved as read.

The President then presented his annual report.

A motion was duly made, seconded and carried that the report be received and filed, as annexed.

The Secretary next presented his report, as annexed.

A motion was duly made, seconded and carried that the report be received and filed.

The Treasurer then presented his report, as annexed.

A motion was duly made, seconded and carried that the report be received and filed.

The Chairman said that election of directors of the Corporation for the coming year was the next order of business.

The following were nominated as directors.

_____          _____

_____          _____

_____          _____


The chairman then stated that the Board has appointed

      and                            as inspectors of election and that they would receive and tally the ballots.

Each shareholder was asked to place his vote in a ballot, stating the number of shares voted, and to sign his name.

The inspectors, after completing a tally of the vote, declared that the following votes had been cast:

| Names of Nominees | Number of Votes |
|---|---|
| _____ | _____ |
| _____ | _____ |
| _____ | _____ |
| _____ | _____ |
| _____ | _____ |

The Chairman then announced that the following persons had been elected directors:

_____          _____

_____          _____

_____          _____

A motion was duly made, seconded and carried that the inspectors file the report with the Clerk of                               County (when required by law) and with the Secretary of the Corporation.

There being no further business, a motion was duly made, seconded and carried that the meeting be adjourned.

Dated the                     day of                     , 19        .


_____

Secretary

# NOTICE TO DIRECTORS
# OF REGULAR BOARD MEETING

Notice is hereby given that a meeting of the Board of

shall be held at                              , City of                              , State of

                    , on the                    day of                    , 19        , at

            o'clock        .m., for the purpose of transacting all such business as may properly

come before the board.


Dated the                              day of                    , 19        .


By Order of the Board of Directors


_____

Secretary

# MINUTES, REGULAR BOARD MEETING

A meeting of the Board of Directors was held at

on the                    day of                    , 19        , at                    o'clock

.m.

The President called the meeting to order.

The following directors were present:


The Secretary reported that notice of the time and place of holding the meeting

had been provided each director in accordance with the By-laws.

A motion was duly made, seconded and carried that the notice be filed.

The President then stated that, a quorum being present, the meeting could

transact business.

Minutes of the preceding meeting of the Board, held                                        ,

19        , were read and adopted.

The President presented his report.

A motion was made, seconded and carried that the President's report be filed.

A motion was made, seconded and carried, that

be appointed to audit the books of the Treasurer before the same are presented to the

shareholders.

A motion was duly made and carried that the meeting elect officers for the

ensuing year.

The following were thereupon elected by ballot:

President: _____

Vice President: _____

Secretary: _____

Treasurer: _____

A motion was duly made and carried that salaries of officers be fixed as follows:

Name _____ Salary per year _____

Name _____ Salary per year _____

Name _____ Salary per year _____

There was no further business. The meeting was adjourned.

Dated: _____ , 19 ___ .

_____
Secretary

# MINUTES OF DIRECTORS' MEETINGS

A regular meeting of the Board of Directors of the Corporation was held at the office of the Corporation, at                                                              ,

on                              , 19      , at              .m.

Present were:

_____          _____

_____          _____

_____          _____

_____          _____

Being a quorum of the directors of the Corporation.

                                        , President of the Corporation, acted as

Chairman of the meeting, and                                        , Secretary of the

Corporation, acted as Secretary of the meeting.

The Secretary presented notice or a waiver of notice of the meeting, signed by all the directors.

The meeting, having been duly convened, was ready to proceed with its business, whereupon it was:

RESOLVED, That the annual salary of                              , as

President of the Corporation, be fixed at                              Dollars

($                    ).

RESOLVED, Further that the annual salary of                              , as

Vice President of the Corporation, be fixed at                              Dollars

($                    ).

RESOLVED, Further that the salary of                              , as

Treasurer of the Corporation, be fixed at                              Dollars

($                    ).

RESOLVED, Further that the annual salary of                    , as

Secretary of the Corporation, be fixed at                              Dollars

($              ).

RESOLVED, That in addition to their present salaries, the officers of the

Corporation,                                                      ,

                      , and

shall participate in all fringe benefit programs available to employees of the Corporation.


A True Record

Attest


_____

Chairman


_____

Secretary

# MINUTES OF SPECIAL MEETING OF STOCKHOLDERS

BE IT KNOWN THAT, a special meeting of the stockholders of

_____ (Corporate Name) was called on _____ , 19 ___ ,

at _____ o'clock at the following address:

_____ , the President, called the meeting to order and

_____ , the Secretary, kept the records of the meeting and its proceedings. It

was duly confirmed and noted by the Secretary that a quorum of stockholders was

present either in person or by proxy, representing more than _____ % of the

outstanding stock entitled to vote on the resolutions proposed at the meeting.

The following stockholders were reported by the Secretary to be present in

person:

| Names | Number of Shares |
|-------|------------------|
| _____ | _____ |
| _____ | _____ |
| _____ | _____ |
| _____ | _____ |

The following stockholders were reported by the Secretary to be represented by

proxy:

| Names | Names of Proxies | Number of Shares |
|-------|------------------|------------------|
| _____ | _____ | _____ |
| _____ | _____ | _____ |
| _____ | _____ | _____ |
| _____ | _____ | _____ |

Upon motion duly made and seconded, the following resolution(s) was/were voted upon:

It was reported that _____ shares of common stock had been voted in favor of the foregoing resolution(s) and _____ shares of common stock had been voted against the resolutions, said vote representing more than _____ % of the outstanding shares entitled to vote thereon.

The President thereupon declared that the resolution(s) had been duly adopted. As all business had been completed, upon motion, the meeting was adjourned.

_____
(Secretary)

_____
(Date)

# Basic Agreements

# AGREEMENT WITH SALES REPRESENTATIVE

Agreement between                        (Company) and

                     (Sales Representative).

Sales representative agrees to:

1.     Represent and sell the Company's             products/services in the geographic area of             .

2.     Accurately represent and state Company policies to all present and potential customers.

3.     Promptly mail in all leads and orders to the Company.

4.     Advise the sales manager of all matters concerning Company customers in the sales territory.

5.     Inform the sales manager if the Sales Representative is representing or plans to represent any other business firm. Sales Representative shall in no event sell a competitive product or service.

6.     Contact the Company with reasonable frequency to discuss sales activities.

7.     Provide one month's notice to the Company of termination.

8.     Return promptly to the company all materials and samples provided by the Company if either party terminates this agreement.

The Company agrees:

1.     To pay the following commissions to the Sales Representative:

        (a)     percent on all prepaid sales, except as stated in (4) below

        (b)     percent on all credit sales, except as stated in (4) below

2.     To negotiate in advance of sale the commission percentage to be paid on all orders where the Company allows a quantity discount or other trade concession.

3.      To deduct commissions on refunds to customers or merchandise returned by the customer where a commission has already been paid to the Representative.

4.      Except by special arrangement, sales of the following items will not be subject to commission:

5.      To furnish Sales Representative with business cards, brochures, catalogs, and any product samples required for sales purposes.

6.      To set minimum monthly quotas after consultation with the Sales Representative.

7.      To give representative one month's notice of termination.

8.      To pay commissions to the Representative on sales from existing customers for a period of _____ months after this agreement is terminated by either party.

Nothing in this agreement shall grant Representative an exclusive sales territory.

Signed this _____ day of _____, 19____ .

_____          _____
Company                                  Sales Representative

# CONFIDENTIALITY AGREEMENT

AGREEMENT between                                             (Company)

and                                             (Undersigned). Pursuant to this

agreement                                             (Company) agrees to disclose to

(Undersigned) certain confidential information

relating to                                             (Company) for the following

purposes:

, and

(Undersigned) shall have access to said confidential information

only for the purposes described above.                                             (Undersigned)

agrees not to use or disclose said confidential information except as provided under the

terms of this agreement.

BE IT KNOWN that                                             (Company) has or

shall supply or disclose to                                             (Undersigned)

certain confidential information, trade secrets, or proprietary information as attached.

Pursuant to this agreement,                                             (Company)

may grant                                             (Undersigned) the right to inspect

(Company's) business records and/or interview

suppliers, customers, employees, or representatives of

(Company) only in the following circumstances:

•       Where                                             (Undersigned) agrees not to use or

disclose such confidential or proprietary information or trade secrets and hold such

information in trust and confidence; and

•       Where                                             (Undersigned) agrees that such

privileged information shall be used only for its intended purpose and shall not be used

for any other purpose nor disclosed to any third party for any purpose whatsoever.

- Where _____ (Undersigned) agrees not to make copies or abstracts or retain any written information supplied by _____ (Company).

- Where _____ (Undersigned) agrees to return upon demand by _____ (Company) all information, including written notes, photographs or memoranda.

- Where _____ (Undersigned) agrees not to disclose confidential information to any employee, consultant, or third party unless such party agrees to execute and be bound by the terms of this agreement.

- Where it is agreed that _____ (Undersigned) shall have no obligation with respect to any information previously known by _____ (Undersigned) or generally known within the community prior to date of this agreement or that shall become common knowledge with the community thereafter.

- Where _____ (Undersigned) acknowledges that information disclosed by _____ (Company) is privileged and confidential and in the event of any breach, _____ (Company) shall be entitled to injunctive relief as a cumulative and not necessarily successive remedy.

This confidentiality and trade secret agreement shall be binding upon and inure to the benefit of the parties, their successors and assigns.

Signed under seal this _____ day of _____ , 19 ____ .

Witness:

_____        _____

_____        _____

# CONSIGNMENT AGREEMENT

Consignment agreement made this                day of                    ,

19      , between                                              (Consignor)

and                                                    (Undersigned).

1.      Undersigned acknowledges the receipt of goods as described on annexed

schedule. Said goods are delivered on consignment and shall remain the property of

Consignor until sold.

2.      Undersigned at its own cost and expense shall keep and display the goods only

in its place of business and, on demand made before any sale, shall return the same in

good order and condition.

3.      Undersigned shall use its best efforts to sell the goods for the Consignor's

account on cash terms and at such prices as shall from time to time be set by Consignor.

4.      Undersigned shall, upon sale, keep the monies due Consignor in trust and

separate and apart from its own funds and deliver such proceeds, less commission, to

Consignor together with an accounting within              days of said sale.

5.      Undersigned shall accept as full payment a commission equal to         % of the

gross sales price exclusive of any sales tax, which the Undersigned shall collect and remit.

6.      Undersigned shall permit the Consignor to enter the premises at reasonable times

to examine and inspect the goods.

7.      Undersigned shall issue such financial statements for public filing as may

reasonably be required by Consignor.

8.      This agreement shall be binding upon and inure to the benefit of the parties, their

successors and assigns.

_____     _____

Record in Public Filing Office

# PARTNERSHIP AGREEMENT

AGREEMENT between the Undersigned ("Partners").

1.    Name: The name of the partnership is

2.    Partners: The names of the partners are

3.    Place of Business: The principal place of business of the partnership is at

4.    Nature of Business: The partnership shall engage in the following business:

5.    Duration: The partnership shall commence business on                          ,

19        , and shall continue until terminated by this agreement or by operation of law.

6.    Contribution of Capital: The partners shall contribute capital in proportionate

shares as follows:

Partner                                                        Share

_____          _____

_____          _____

_____          _____

7.    Allocation of Depreciation or Gain or Loss on Contributed Property: The

partners understand that for income tax purposes the partnership's adjusted basis of some

of the contributed property differs from fair market value at which the property was

accepted to the partnership. However, the partners intend that the general allocation rule

of the Internal Revenue Code shall apply and that the depreciation or gain or loss arising

with respect to this property shall be allocated proportionately between the partners, as

allocated in Paragraph 6 above, in determining the taxable income or loss of the partnership and the distributive share of each partner in the same manner as if such property had been purchased by the partnership at a cost equal to the adjusted tax basis.

8.      Capital Accounts: An individual capital account shall be maintained for each partner. The capital of each partner shall consist of his original contribution of capital, as described in Paragraph 6, increased by additional capital contributions and decreased by distributions in reduction of partnership capital and reduced by his share of partnership losses, if these losses are charged to the capital accounts.

9.      Drawing Accounts: An individual drawing account shall be maintained for each partner. All withdrawals by a partner shall be charged to said partner's drawing account. Withdrawals shall be limited to amounts unanimously agreed to by the partners.

10.     Salaries: No partner shall receive any salary for services rendered to the partnership except as specifically and first approved by a majority of the partners.

11.     Loans by Partners: A partner may lend money to the partnership at an interest and terms rate agreed on in writing by all partners, at the time any loan is made.

12.     Profits and Losses: The net profits of the partnership shall be divided proportionately among the partners, and the net losses shall be borne proportionately as follows:

13.     Management: The partners shall have equal rights and control in the management of the partnership.

14.     Books of Accounts: The partnership shall maintain adequate accounting records. All books, records, and accounts of the partnership shall be open at all times to inspection by all partners.

15.     Accounting Basis: The books of account shall be kept on a cash basis.

16.     Fiscal Year: The books of account shall be kept on a fiscal year basis, commencing January 1 and ending December 31, and shall be closed and balanced at the end of each year.

17.     Annual Audit: The books of account shall be audited as of the close of each fiscal year by an accountant selected by the partners.

18.     Banking: All funds of the partnership shall be deposited in the name of the partnership into a checking or savings account as designated by the partners. Checks shall be drawn on the partnership account for partnership purposes only.

19.     Retirement: Any partner may retire from the partnership upon sixty (60) days' prior notice to the other partners. A retiring partner shall be entitled to the then existing weekly draw for                          weeks from the date of his notice of termination.

20.     Death or Insanity: The death, incapacity or insanity of a partner shall cause an immediate dissolution of the partnership.

21.     Election of Remaining Partners to Continue Business: In the event of the retirement, death or insanity of a partner, the remaining partners shall have the right to continue the business of the partnership, either by themselves or in conjunction with any other person or persons selected, but they shall pay to the retiring partner, or to the legal representatives of the deceased or insane partner, the value of his interest in the partnership.

22.     Valuation of Partner's Interest: The value of the interest of a retiring, deceased, or insane partner shall be the sum of (a) the partner's capital account, (b) any unpaid loans due the partner, and (c) the partner's proportionate share of the accrued net profits remaining undistributed in his drawing account. No value for goodwill shall be included in determining the value of a partner's interest.

23.     Payment of Purchase Price: The value of the partner's interest shall be paid without interest to the retiring partner, or to the legal representative of the deceased,

incapacitated or insane partner, in monthly installments, commencing on the first day of the second month after the effective date of the purchase.

24.     Termination: In the event that the remaining partners do not elect to purchase the interest of the retiring, deceased, or insane partner, or in the event the partners mutually agree to dissolve the partnership, the partnership shall terminate, and the partners shall proceed with reasonable promptness to liquidate the business of the partnership. The assets of the partnership shall first be used to pay or provide for all debts of the partnership. Thereafter, all money remaining undistributed in the drawing accounts shall be paid to the partners. Then the remaining assets shall be divided proportionately as follows:

25.     This agreement shall be binding upon and inure to the benefit of the parties, their successors, assigns and personal representatives.

Signed under seal this                 day of                 , 19        .

Witness:

_____        _____

_____        _____

_____        _____

# CONTRACTOR AGREEMENT

Date:

To

Address

City or Town


Dear:

We propose to furnish all materials and labor necessary to complete the

following:


The above work shall be completed in a substantial and workmanlike manner

according to standard practices and applicable codes for the sum of

Dollars ($          ).

Payments to be made


to the value of                per cent (          %) of all work completed. The

entire amount of contract to be paid within                days after completion.

Any alteration or modification from the above specifications involving extra cost

of material or labor will be executed only upon written change orders and will become an extra charge over the sum mentioned in this contract. All agreements must be made in writing.

Respectfully submitted,

By: _____

## ACCEPTANCE

You are hereby authorized to furnish all materials and labor required to complete the work mentioned in the above proposal, for which

agree to pay the amount contained in said proposal and according to the terms thereof.

ACCEPTED          _____

_____

Date                    , 19      .

# CONTRACT FOR SALE
# OF PERSONAL PROPERTY

AGREEMENT between

(Seller), and                                                                 (Buyer).

For good consideration the parties agree that:

1.      Seller shall sell and Buyer shall buy the following property:


2.      Buyer shall pay to Seller the total purchase price of $                      ;

payable as follows:

$                          deposit now paid

$                          balance on sale by cash, bank or certified check.

3.      Seller warrants it has good and legal title to said property, full authority to sell

same, and that said property shall be sold free and clear of all liens, encumbrances,

liabilities and adverse claims by warranty bill of sale.

4.      Said property is sold in "as is" condition, Seller disclaiming any warranty of

merchantability or working order or condition of the property except that it shall be sold

in its present condition reasonable wear and tear excepted.

5.      The parties shall transfer title on                          , 19      , at the address

of the Seller.

6.      This agreement shall be binding upon and inure to the benefit of the parties, their

successors, assigns and personal representatives.


Signed under seal this                      day of                      , 19        .


_____        _____

Buyer                                              Seller

# ARBITRATION AGREEMENT

The undersigned with interests in a certain contract or claim described as

, (claim)

agree to resolve by binding arbitration any dispute or controversy we now have or may

ever have in connection with said claim.

Said Arbitration shall be in accordance with the rules of the American

Arbitration Association for the City of                                        , which rules

are incorporated herein, and the decision or award by the Arbitrators shall be conclusive

and binding upon us and enforceable in a court of law.


Signed under seal this                          day of                          , 19          .

_____

_____

# COVENANT NOT TO COMPLETE

FOR GOOD CONSIDERATION,

(Undersigned) jointly and severally agree not to compete with the business of

(Company) and its successors and assigns.

Pursuant to this agreement, the term "not compete" shall mean that

(Undersigned) shall not directly, indirectly or through

use of a third party engage in a business or other activity described as:

This covenant not to compete applies with full force to the following categories: owner, officer, director, employee, agent, consultant, partner, or stockholder (except as a passive investor in a publicly-owned company).

This covenant not to compete shall extend only within                    miles from the present location of                              (Company) at

(Address).

Upon any breach,                         (Company) shall be entitled to full injunctive relief without need to post bond, which rights shall be cumulative with and not successive or exclusive of any other legal rights.

This agreement shall be binding upon and inure to the benefit of the parties, their successors, assigns and personal representatives.

Signed under seal this                    day of                    , 19         .

In the presence of:

_____          _____

_____          _____

# INDEMNITY AGREEMENT

Agreement of Indemnification dated                              , 199    ,

between                                    (Undersigned) and

                                    (Indemnitees).

FOR VALUE RECEIVED,                                    (Undersigned)

jointly and severally agree to indemnify and save harmless

                    (Indemnitees) and its successors and assigns from any claim,

action, liability, loss, damage or suit arising from the following:

Where any claim is asserted,                                    (Indemnitees)

shall provide                              (Undersigned) with reasonably timely

notice of same in writing. Thereafter,                                    (Undersigned)

shall at its own expense defend, protect and save harmless

                    (Indemnitees) against said claim or any loss or liability resulting therefrom.

Should                              (Undersigned) fail to so defend and/or

indemnify and save harmless, then, in such case,

(Indemnitees) shall have full rights to defend, pay or settle said claim on their own

behalf without notice to                              (Undersigned) for all fees, costs, and

payments made or agreed to be paid to discharge said claim.

                                    (Undersigned) agrees to pay all reasonable

attorneys' fees necessary to enforce said indemnification.

This agreement shall be unlimited as to amount or duration, and it shall be

binding upon and inure to the benefit of the parties, their successors, assigns and

personal agents and representatives.

Signed under seal this               day of                    , 19      .

In the presence of:

_____        _____

_____        _____

# CONDITIONAL SALE AGREEMENT

Date:

Be it known that: _____ (Buyer) agrees to

purchase from: _____ (Seller) the following described items:

(Describe or attach)


| | |
|---|---|
| Sales price | $ _____ |
| Sales tax | $ _____ |
| Finance charge | $ _____ |
| Insurance | $ _____ |
| Other charges | $ _____ |
| Total purchase price | $ _____ |

Less:

| | | |
|---|---|---|
| Deposit | $ _____ | |
| Other credits | $ _____ | |

| | |
|---|---|
| Total credits | $ _____ |
| Amount financed | $ _____ |

ANNUAL INTEREST RATE _____%

The amount financed shall be paid in _____ (weekly/
monthly) installments of $ _____ each, beginning one (week/month) from the
above date.

The seller shall retain title to the items sold until full payment of the purchase
price, subject to payment credits and release of this security interest as required by law.

The undersigned agrees to safely keep the items free from other liens and encumbrances at the below address and to not remove goods without seller's consent.

Buyer further agrees to execute all financing statements as may be required to perfect this conditional sales agreement, and the Buyer shall keep goods adequately insured, naming Seller loss-payee.

The full balance of the purchase price shall become due upon any default; and the undersigned shall pay all reasonable attorney's fees and costs of collection. Upon default, Seller may reclaim the goods, hold and dispose of same, and collect expenses, together with any deficiency due from Buyer, subject to the Buyer's right to redeem said items pursuant to law and the Uniform Commercial Code.

THIS IS A CONDITIONAL SALE AGREEMENT.

Accepted:

_____          _____

Seller                                                    Buyer

                                                           _____

                                                           Address

                                                           By _____

This Agreement or Financing Statements must be recorded as required by state law to protect your rights.

# STOCK SUBSCRIPTION AGREEMENT

FOR GOOD VALUE, the undersigned hereby subscribes for the purchase of

shares of

(Corporation) for the total aggregate purchase price of                    dollars

($                    ) per share.

Said shares shall have full voting rights, be non-assessable and, upon issue shall

constitute                % of the total outstanding shares of the Corporation, all classes

inclusive.

Said shares are further subject to all rights and obligations contained within the

By-laws or Articles of Incorporation, and the undersigned acknowledges disclosure and

acceptance of same.

The full subscription price shall be paid upon demand of the Treasurer of the

Corporation and delivery of said shares.

Signed under seal this                    day of                    , 19        .

_____

The Foregoing stock subscription is accepted on the behalf of the Corporation

this                    day of                    , 19        .

_____

On Behalf of the Corporation

# PURCHASE REQUIREMENT AGREEMENT

FOR GOOD VALUE, customer and supplier agree to enter into this purchase requirement agreement on the following terms:

1.       During the period from         , 19    , to        , 19    , customer shall purchase from supplier, the below described items in the following quantity:




2.       Customer shall pay for said purchases within the supplier's customary credit terms or under such extended terms as shall be expressly agreed in writing by Supplier.

3.       All purchases hereunder shall further be at the prevailing price and include all promotional or advertising allowances, cash and/or trade discounts and other incentives and inducements, if any, all as then available to other accounts purchasing from supplier on equally proportionate terms.

4.       Should customer fail to meet the above described purchase requirements or otherwise default under this agreement then, in such event, Supplier shall have full rights to demand immediate payment of all sums due Supplier, notwithstanding extended terms evidenced by any note, extension agreement or other agreement authorizing extended terms.


      Signed this          day of         , 19   .

_____        _____

Customer                         Supplier

# OPEN LISTING AGREEMENT

1.      This listing agreement made on this                          day of                     ,
19      , between                                                      (Owner) and

                                                      (Real Estate Broker) who agree
as follows:

2.      Listing term: Owner lists the property described in Paragraph 3, with Broker for
a period of                          days.

3.      Description of Property: The property listed is described as:


4.      Commission: Owner agrees to pay Broker a commission of                     % of
the sale price if Broker finds a purchaser ready, willing, and able to pay at least
$                          for the property (or such other price as may be acceptable to
Owner).

6.      Non-Exclusive: Owner retains the right to sell the property on his/her own
account with no sales commission due broker provided Broker did not find buyer. Owner
may further list the property with other brokers. If a sale is made within

                    months after this agreement terminates to a party found by Broker
during the term of this agreement, such party having been disclosed to Owner before
expiration of the agreement, then Owner shall pay the commission specified above.

7.      Forfeit of Deposit: Should a deposit be forfeited by a purchaser, then one-half of
said deposit shall be retained by Broker (if this amount does not exceed the commission)
and one-half shall be paid to Owner.

_____
Owner

_____
Broker

# AGREEMENT TO ASSUME DEBT

FOR GOOD VALUE, and in consideration of                                   ,

(Creditor) assenting to the transfer of certain assets from

(Customer) to the transferee, it is agreed that:

1.     Customer and the transferee acknowledge that Customer duly owes Creditor

$                (debt).

2.     The transferee unconditionally and irrevocably agrees to assume and pay said

debt, guarantees Creditor the prompt payment of said debt, and will fully indemnify and

save harmless the Creditor from any loss resulting from non-payment.

3.     Said debt shall be paid as follows:


4.     This agreement shall not release or discharge the obligations of Customer to

Creditor for the payment of said debt, provided that if transferee shall pay the debt as

above described, then Creditor shall not commence collection against Customer. Upon

default, Creditor shall have full rights, jointly and severally, against both Customer and

the transferee for any balance then owing.

5.     This agreement shall be binding upon and inure to the benefit of the parties, their

successors, assigns and personal representatives.

Signed under seal this                day of                , 19        .


_____

Transferee

Assented to:


_____          _____

Creditor                                               Customer

# EXTENSION OF AGREEMENT

For good value, this Extension Agreement is made by and between

(First Party) and

(Second Party).

Whereas a certain Agreement between the parties dated                    ,

19        , expires on                           , 19      , and the parties want to extend

and continue said Agreement; it is agreed that said Agreement is extended for an

additional term commencing upon the expiration of the original term and shall now

expire on                           , 19      .

This extension shall be on all other terms and conditions as stated in the original

Agreement.

This extension agreement shall be binding upon and inure to the benefit of the

parties, their successors, and personal representatives.

Signed under seal this                    day of                    , 19      .

_____          _____

                                         First Party

                                         _____

                                         Second Party

# AGREEMENT TO EXTEND
# PERFORMANCE DATE

FOR GOOD VALUE,                          (First Party)

and                          (Second Party) to a certain (Describe)

agreement dated                  ,

19     , (Agreement), hereby agree that:

1.     Wherein said agreement provides that completion or full performance shall

occur before                  , 19    .

2.     That the parties mutually agree that the performance date be extended to

              , 19    , without other change in terms or further extension.

This Agreement shall be binding upon and inure to the benefit of the parties,

their successors, assigns, and personal representatives.

Signed under seal this            day of           , 19    .

In the presence of:

_____      _____

                                             _____

# MUTUAL TERMINATION
# OF CONTRACT

FOR GOOD VALUE, the Undersigned as parties to a certain contract dated

, 19      ; described as:

do hereby cancel, rescind and mutually terminate said contract effective this date.

This termination shall be without further recourse by or against either party and this shall constitute mutual releases of any further obligations under said contract, all as if the said contract had not been entered into.

Signed under seal this                    day of                    , 19      .

_____

_____

# Employment

# EMPLOYMENT AGREEMENT

For good value, Employment Agreement is made between

("Company") and

("Employee").

1.      Company employs Employee, and Employee accepts employment on the following terms and conditions.

2.      *Term of Employment.* Subject to termination as provided below, this agreement shall commence                        , 19      , and terminate on                              , 19      .

3.      *Salary.* Company shall pay Employee a salary of $                  per year, payable at regular payroll periods.

4.      *Duties and Position.* Company employs Employee as                              . Employee's duties may be reasonably modified at Company's discretion.

5.      *Employee to Devote Full Time to Company.* Employee shall be employed full time and shall not engage in any other business activity.

6.      *Confidentiality of Proprietary Information.* Employee agrees not to reveal confidential information to any person, firm, corporation, or association neither during nor after the term of employment. Should Employee reveal or threaten to reveal confidential information, the Company may restrain Employee from disclosing same or from rendering any services to any party to whom said information has been or is threatened to be disclosed. An injunction is not the exclusive remedy, and the Company may pursue any other remedies against Employee for breach or threatened breach of this condition, including recovery of damages from Employee.

7.      *Reimbursement of Expenses.* Employee may incur reasonable expenses for promoting the Company's business, including entertainment, travel, and similar

expenses. Company shall reimburse Employee for all business expenses after the Employee presents an itemized account of expenditures.

8.      *Vacation.* Employee is entitled to an annual vacation of

weeks at full pay. The Employee will take his yearly vacation over a consecutive period

beginning on or after                                                and ending on or before


9.      *Disability.* If the Employee cannot perform the duties because of illness or

incapacity for a period of more than                         weeks, the compensation

otherwise due during said illness or incapacity shall be reduced                percent.

Employee's full compensation shall be reinstated when he returns to work and fully

discharges his duties. If Employee is absent from work for any reason for a continuous

period beyond                         months, the Company may terminate Employee

and the Company's obligations under this agreement shall cease.

10.     *Termination of Agreement.* Without cause, Employee or the Company may

terminate this agreement. Company will pay the Employee on the date of termination a

severance of $                     . Notwithstanding, despite anything to the contrary in

this agreement, the Company may terminate Employee's employment upon

           day's notice to the Employee upon:

    (a)   The sale of substantially all of the Company's assets

    (b)   The sale, exchange, or other disposition in one transaction of the majority

            of the Company's outstanding corporate shares; or

    (c)   Business termination or liquidation

    (d)   Merger or consolidation of the Company with another company.

11.     *Death Benefit.* Should Employee die during his employ, the Company shall pay

to the Employee's estate any compensation due him up to the end of the month in which

Employee dies.

12. *Restriction on Postemployment Competition.* For _____ years after termination, the Employee shall not, within a _____ mile radius of the Company's present place of business, own, manage, operate, control, consult to or be employed by any business similar to or competitive with that conducted by the Company.

13. *Assistance in Litigation.* Employee shall, upon reasonable notice, furnish such information and assistance to the Company as it may reasonably require concerning any litigation in which it is, or may become, a party.

14. *Effect of Prior Agreements.* This agreement supersedes any prior agreement between the Company and Employee, except that this agreement shall not reduce any benefit or compensation due Employee of a kind elsewhere provided and not expressly provided for in this agreement.

15. *Arbitration.* All claims or controversy that arise out of or relate to this agreement, or the breach of it, shall be settled by arbitration in accordance with the rules of the American Arbitration Association. Judgment upon any award may be entered in any court with jurisdiction.

16. *Effect of Waiver by Company.* Should Company waive a breach of any provision of this agreement by the Employee, such waiver shall not be construed a waiver of later breach by Employee.

17. *Severability.* If any provision of this agreement is held invalid, all other provisions of this agreement shall remain in effect. If this agreement is held invalid, then, to the extent permitted by law, any prior agreement between the Company (or any predecessor thereof) and Employee shall be deemed reinstated as if this agreement had not been executed.

18.    *Assumption of Agreement.* Company's rights and obligations under this agreement shall inure to the benefit and be binding upon the Company's successors and assignees.

19.    *Oral Modifications Not Binding.* This is the entire agreement between Company and Employee. Oral changes have no effect. It may be altered only by a signed agreement, waiver, change, modification, extension, or discharge.

Signed under seal this _____ day of _____ , 19 ____ .

_____    _____

Company                                      Employee

# JOB APPLICANT WAIVER FORM

I, the job applicant, hereby certify that the information contained in my employment application is accurate to the best of my knowledge. I further understand that false information is grounds for refusal to hire or, if I am hired, grounds to dismiss.

I authorize any persons or organizations referenced in my application to provide any and all information concerning my previous employment or education or such other information they might have, personal or otherwise, with regard to any of the subjects covered by this application and release all such parties from liability for any damage that may result from furnishing such information to you. I authorize you to obtain such information.

In consideration for my being considered for employment by your company, I agree to abide by the rules and regulations of the company and acknowledge that these rules may be changed or modified by the company. I further acknowledge that my employ may be terminated, and any offer of employment, if such is made, may be withdrawn, without prior notice, at any time, at the option of the company or me.

I understand that no representative of the company has authority to enter into any agreement for employment for fixed period of time, either prior to or after commencement of employ, or to offer any benefits, terms or conditions of employ contrary to the foregoing.

_____          _____

Signature of Applicant                                        Date


_____          _____

Signature of Company Representative                  Date

# EMPLOYMENT ACKNOWLEDGEMENT
## (PART-TIME OR TEMPORARY)

I understand I am being employed by

(Company) in a temporary capacity only and for such time as my services are required

by                                    (Company). I also understand that my employ

does not make me eligible for and does not entitle me to any special consideration for

permanent employment. I acknowledge that my temporary or part-time employment may

be discontinued at any time either with or without cause under procedures set forth for

permanent employees. I also acknowledge that I am not entitled to nor am I eligible to

participate in any benefit programs, retirement programs, or any other programs

available to permanent employees (unless required by law). Should I be allowed to

participate in any benefit or program, then my continued participation may be voluntarily

withdrawn or terminated by                          (Company) at any time.


Dated:


_____


Witnesses:


_____


_____


                              _____

                              Employee

# NIGHT SHIFT AGREEMENT

Employee:


NIGHT WORK MAY BE REQUIRED TO MEET OUR PRESENT OR
FUTURE NEEDS. ALL EMPLOYEES ARE HIRED WITH THE UNDERSTANDING
THAT THEY ARE ABLE AND WILLING TO WORK NIGHTS, IF NECESSARY.
PLEASE ANSWER EACH OF THE FOLLOWING QUESTIONS

|  | YES | NO |
|---|---|---|

(1)    Do you have any physical disabilities, impairments or

illnesses that would interfere with your working at

night?

(2)    Are there home or personal conditions that would

interfere with your working at night?

(3)    Do you object to a night shift, if necessary?

   I acknowledge that any offer of employment made to me this date is conditional
upon my agreeing to work at night if required.


Dated:


Witnessed:


_____   _____

# INDEPENDENT CONTRACTOR
# ACKNOWLEDGEMENT

Undersigned hereby enters into a certain arrangement or affiliation with

(Company), as of this date. The

Undersigned confirms:

1.      Undersigned is an independent contractor and is not an employee, agent, partner or joint venturer of or with the Company.

2.      Undersigned shall not be entitled to participate in any vacation, medical or other fringe benefit or retirement program of the Company and shall not make claim of entitlement to any such employee program or benefit.

3.      Undersigned shall be solely responsible for the payment of withholding taxes, FICA and other such tax deductions on any earnings or payments made, and the Company shall withhold no such payroll tax deductions from any payments due. The Undersigned agrees to indemnify and reimburse the Company from any claim or assessment by any taxing authority arising from this paragraph.

4.      Undersigned and Company acknowledge that the Undersigned shall not be subject to the provisions of any personnel policy or rules and regulations applicable to employees, as the Undersigned shall fulfill his/her responsibility independent of and without supervisory control by the Company.

Signed under seal this                    day of                    , 19        .

_____          _____
Independent Contractor                   Company

# CONFLICT OF INTEREST DECLARATION

I have fully read and understand the Company policy statement on conflicts of interest and declare that neither I nor, to the best of my knowledge, any member of my immediate family has any conflict between our personal or business affairs or interests and my responsibilities for the Company. I shall also continue to conduct my affairs according to said policy.

To my best knowledge no relative is employed by the Company, and neither I nor any relative owns, is employed by or is affiliated with any supplier or customer of the Company. I agree to promptly notify the Company upon learning of any such affiliation.

_____

Employee's Signature

_____

Date

# NOTICE OF
# CONFIDENTIALITY AGREEMENT

Date:

To:

Re:

We understand that our above captioned former employee is now employed by you.

We want to advise you of certain obligations that this individual has to our company relative to confidential trade secrets or proprietary information which may have been obtained or developed during his or her employ with our company and of an existing agreement to hold same confidential.

It is not our intent to prevent this individual or any other prior employee from applying the general knowledge of the industry or skill acquired while employed by our company which, of course, may be exercised freely. Protecting our confidential information is our only concern. Since your organization also has confidential data and trade secrets, I am sure you understand our position. Your cooperation will be greatly appreciated.

Very truly,

_____

# EMPLOYEE AGREEMENT
## NOT TO DISCLOSE

For good value, and in consideration of employment with

(Company),                                             (Undersigned

Employee) hereby agrees:

•     That during said employ there may be disclosed to me certain trade secrets,

confidential, or privileged information of

(Company) including:

> client and prospect lists; financial and business information; marketing
>
> methods, processes, formulae, compositions, systems, techniques,
>
> inventions, machines, proprietary computer software and research projects,
>
> pricing data, sources of supply, financial data and marketing, production, or
>
> merchandising systems or plans.

•     I further agree that as long as I work for

(Company) and after my employment with

(Company) ends (whether with or without cause), I shall not directly or indirectly

disclose or divulge to others (whether for my own benefit or that of another, including

future employers) any trade secrets, confidential, privileged, or proprietary information

of                                             (Company) which would breach this

agreement.

•     Upon termination of my employ:

> a) I agree to and shall promptly return to
>
> (Company) all documents and other property of
>
> (Company) including but not necessarily limited to: drawings, blueprints,
>
> reports, manuals, correspondence, customer lists, computer programs, and
>
> all other materials and all copies thereof relating in any way to the

Company's business, or in any way obtained by me during the course of my employ. I further agree that I shall not retain any copies, notes or abstracts of the foregoing.

b) I agree that                               (Company) may notify any prospective employer or third party of the existence of said agreement and shall be entitled to enjoin any breach.

c) This agreement shall be binding upon me and my personal agents, representatives and successors in interest and shall inure to the benefit of the Company, its successors and assigns.

Signed under seal this               day of              , 19      .

_____      _____

Company                                   Employee

# EMPLOYEE AGREEMENT
# ON PROPRIETARY RIGHTS

Date:

Proposal for:

I have suggestions, ideas or inventions and may in the future have other suggestions for the Company to consider. I understand the Company cannot receive such suggestions in confidence; therefore, I agree to submit my suggestions to the Company under the following conditions:

(1)    Company review of my suggestions shall be made only pursuant to my request, and submitted proposals or suggestions will not be treated as secret or confidential.

(2)    No obligation or contract of any kind is assumed by nor may be implied against the Company unless or until I have entered into a formal written contract with the Company concerning such suggestions. Any obligation must be expressed in a written contract.

(3)    Neither the Company nor any of its affiliates shall have any rights under any patents I now have or may later obtain for any suggestions, unless said rights are expressly reserved by agreement, but, in consideration of their examining my suggestions, I release them from any liability in connection with my suggestions or their use of my suggestions or of any portion thereof, except such liability as may accrue under valid patents now or hereafter issued.

I acknowledge that, prior to this date, I have not made any disclosure to the Company nor any of its affiliates regarding my suggestions and that the entire disclosure now made by me to the Company is included in the attached documents described below and submitted for the Company's record.

Should I make additional disclosures regarding such suggestions, I will furnish the Company a complete description of such additional disclosure for addition to the records.

_____

Signature of Employee

_____

Address of Employee

The following are attached:

1)

2)

3)

4)

5)

6)

7)

8)

# EMPLOYEE AGREEMENT ON
# INVENTIONS AND PATENTS

Agreement between ,"Company"

and ,"Employee".

In consideration of the employment or continued employment of Employee by Company, the parties agree that:

1. Employee may have access to facilities, apparatus, equipment, drawings, systems, formulae, reports, manuals, invention records, customer lists, computer programs, or other material embodying trade secrets or confidential technical or business information of Company or its Affiliates. Employee shall not use such information or material for himself or others nor take any such material or reproductions from Company during or after employ by Company except as required in Employee's duties to Company. Employee shall immediately return all material and reproductions in his possession to Company upon request and in any event upon termination of employment.

2. Except with company's prior written authorization, Employee shall not disclose nor publish any trade secret or confidential technical or business information or material of Company or its Affiliates or of another party to whom Company owes an obligation of confidence, either during or after employ.

3. Employee shall promptly furnish to Company a complete record of all inventions, patents and improvements (patentable or not) which he, solely or jointly, may conceive, make, or first disclose during his employ with Company.

4. Employee grants to Company and its nominee his entire right, title, and interest in and to inventions, patents and improvements that in any way relate to the actual, planned or anticipated business or activities of Company or its Affiliates or that are anticipated by or result from any task or work by employee for or on behalf of

Company together with any and all domestic and foreign patent rights in such inventions and improvements. Employee shall promptly do all lawful acts reasonably requested, at any time during and after employment by Company, without additional compensation but at Company's expense, to secure for Company said patent rights.

5. If employee accepts employment with any firm or engages in any type of activity in his own behalf or in behalf of any organization in competition with Company or its Affiliates during a period of                              year(s) following termination of his employment with Company, employee shall notify Company in writing within thirty days of the name and address of such party and the nature of such activity.

6. Employee shall give Company timely written notice of any of his prior employment agreements or patent rights that may conflict with the interests of Company or its Affiliates.

7. No waiver by either party of any breach by the other party of any provision of this Agreement shall waive any succeeding breach of such provision or be a waiver of the provision itself.

8. This Agreement shall be binding upon and pass to the benefit of the successors and assigns of Company and the legal representatives and assigns of Employee.

9. This Agreement supersedes any prior employment agreement or understanding between Employee and Company. This Agreement may be modified or amended only in writing signed by an executive officer of Company and by Employee.

10. Should any portion of this Agreement be held to be invalid, unenforceable or void, such holding shall not invalidate the remainder of this Agreement nor any other part. The parties agree that the provisions held to be invalid, unenforceable, or void shall, if possible, be deemed amended or reduced in scope, to the extent they are deemed valid.

11. This agreement shall be binding upon and inure to the benefit of the parties, their successors, assigns and personal representatives.

_____          _____
Company Name                     Employee's Full Name

                                 Employee acknowledges reading,
                                 understanding and receiving a signed
                                 copy of this Agreement


By _____       _____
    Company Officer or Witness    Employee's Full Signature

# EMPLOYEE WARNING NOTICE

To: (Employee)


We want to advise you that your work performance is unsatisfactory for the following reasons:

1.  _____

2.  _____

3.  _____

4.  _____


You must correct the problem, within the following time period:

or we shall have no alternative but to consider termination of your employment.

Correction of the problem by you will entail the following:


If you have any questions on this matter or if we can help you improve your performance, please discuss this matter with your supervisor at your earliest possible opportunity.


Dated:


_____

# AUTHORIZATION TO RELEASE
# EMPLOYEE INFORMATION

Date:

BE IT KNOWN, that the undersigned

(Employee) authorizes the release of the following employment information to

(Circle as many of the following as apply.)

- Salary history

- Position/title

- Department

- Location

- Supervisor's name

- Dates of employment

- Part-time/full-time or hours worked

- Whether you worked under a maiden name

- Garnishees, if any

- Reason for separation from service

- Medical/accident/illness reports

- Other: _____

_____          _____

Employee Signature                                          Date

# EMPLOYEE RESIGNATION

Date:

To:

Title:

The undersigned hereby resigns the position of                                    ,

effective as of                              , 19      .

_____

Signature

The foregoing resignation is accepted this                              day of

, 19      .

_____

_____

Title

# Loans and Borrowing

# CONSUMER LOAN AGREEMENT

1.      Parties: The Undersigned is

           , the Borrower, and the Lender is

      .

2.      Date of Agreement:

3.      Promise to Pay: Within          months from today, I shall pay to Lender         ($      ) and interest and other charges as stated below.

4.      Responsibility: Although this agreement may be signed below by more than one person, I understand that each of us is responsible for paying back the full amount.

5.      Breakdown of Loan: This is what I will pay:

      1.    Amount of Loan:      $ _____

      2.    Other (Describe):     $ _____

      3.    Amount financed:     $ _____

           (Add 1 and 2)

      4.    Finance charge:      $ _____

      5.    Total of payments:    $ _____

           (Add 3 and 4)

           ANNUAL PERCENTAGE RATE  _____ %

6.      Repayment: This is how I will repay:

      I will repay the amount of this note in         equal, uninterrupted monthly installments of $      each on the day of each month starting on the      day of      , 19   , and ending on     , 19   .

7.      Prepayment: I have the right to prepay the whole outstanding amount at any time. If I do, or if this loan is refinanced—that is, replaced by a new note—you will

refund the unearned finance charge, figured by the rule of 78 (a commonly used formula for calculating rebates on installment loans).

8.      Late Charge: Any installment not paid within ten (10) days of its due date shall be subject to a late charge of 5% of the payment, but not to exceed $ for any such late installment.

9.      Security: To protect the Lender, I furnish the Lender what is known as a security interest or mortgage in: (Describe)



10.     Default: If for any reason I fail to make any payment on time, I shall be in default. The Lender can then demand immediate payment of the entire remaining unpaid balance of this loan, without giving anyone further notice. If I have not paid the full amount of the loan when the final payment is due, the Lender will charge me interest on the unpaid balance at                percent (         %) per year.

11.     Right of Offset: If this loan becomes past due, the Lender will have the right to pay this loan from any deposit or security I have with this Lender without telling me ahead of time. Even if the Lender gives me an extension of time to pay this loan, I still must repay the entire loan.

12.     Collection Fees: If this note is placed with an attorney for collection, then I agree to pay an attorney's fee of fifteen percent (15%) of the unpaid balance. This fee will be added to the unpaid balance of the loan.

13.     Co-borrowers: If I am signing this agreement as a co-borrower, I agree to be equally responsible with the other borrowers for this loan.

Agreed To:


_____        _____

Borrower                               Lender

# PROMISSORY NOTE

Loan No:

Date:

(Borrower) agrees and promises to pay

to                               (Lender) the sum of

($              ) Dollars for value received, with interest at the annual rate of        %

payable after                    (Date).

If this note is in default and is placed for collection,

(Borrower) shall pay all reasonable costs of collection and attorneys'

fees.


_____        _____

(Borrower)                          (Date)

_____        _____

(Lender)                           (Date)

_____        _____

(Witness)                          (Date)

# SECURED PROMISSORY NOTE

FOR GOOD VALUE, the undersigned jointly and severally promises to pay to the order of                                        the sum of

($                    ) Dollars, together with interest at the rate of

% per annum on the unpaid balance, paid in the manner following:

Payments shall be first applied to interest and the balance to principal. This note may be prepaid at any time, in whole or in part, without penalty.

This note shall, at the option of any holder hereof, be due and payable upon the:

1.       Failure to make any payment within                    days of its due date.

2.       Breach of any security interest, mortgage, loan agreement, pledge agreement or guarantee granted as collateral security for this note.

3.       Breach of any loan agreement, security agreement or mortgage, if any, having a priority over any loan agreement, security agreement or mortgage granted, in whole or in part, as collateral security for this note.

4.       Death, incapacity, dissolution or liquidation of any of the undersigned, or any endorser, guarantor or surety.

5.       Filing by any of the undersigned of an assignment for the benefit of creditors, bankruptcy or other form of insolvency, or by suffering an involuntary petition in bankruptcy or receivership not vacated within thirty (30) days.

If this note shall be in default and placed for collection, the undersigned shall pay all reasonable attorney fees and costs of collection. Payments not made within five (5) days of the due date shall be subject to a                    % late charge.

Payments shall be made to such address as may from time to time be designated by any holder.

The undersigned and all other parties to this note, whether as endorsers, guarantors or sureties, shall remain fully bound until this note is paid and waive demand, presentment and protest and all notices thereto and further agree to remain bound, notwithstanding any extension, modification, waiver, or other indulgence or discharge or release of any obligor hereunder or exchange, substitution, or release of any collateral granted as security for this note. No modification or indulgence by any holder hereof shall be binding unless in writing; and any indulgence on any one occasion shall not be an indulgence for any other or future occasion. The rights of any holder hereof shall be cumulative and not necessarily successive. This note shall take effect as a sealed instrument and be governed and enforced in accordance with the laws of

.

Dated:

_____

_____

This promissory note is secured by security agreement of the same date.

# GENERAL GUARANTY

FOR GOOD VALUE, and to induce

(Creditor) to extend credit to                                                        (Customer),

the undersigned guarantees to Creditor the prompt, punctual and full payment of all

monies as may now or hereinafter be due Creditor from Customer.

Until terminated, this guaranty is unlimited in amount and duration and shall

remain in force notwithstanding any extension, compromise, adjustment, forbearance,

waiver, release or discharge of any party, obligor or guarantor, or release in whole or in

part of any security granted for said indebtedness or compromise or adjustment therein.

The undersigned waives all notices thereto.

The obligations of the undersigned shall be primary and not necessarily

secondary, and Creditor shall not be required to exhaust its remedies against Customer

before enforcing its rights under this guaranty against the undersigned.

The guaranty hereunder shall be unconditional and absolute. The undersigned

waives all rights of subrogation or set-off until all sums due under this guaranty are fully

paid and waives generally all suretyship defenses or defenses in the nature hereof.

In the event all payments due under this guaranty are not punctually paid upon

demand, then undersigned shall pay all reasonable costs and attorney's fees necessary for

collection.

If there are two or more guarantors to this guaranty, the obligations shall be joint

and several and binding upon and inure to the benefit of the parties, their successors,

assigns and personal representatives.

This guaranty may be terminated by any guarantor upon fifteen (15) days written

notice of termination, mailed certified mail, return receipt requested to the Creditor. Such

termination shall extend only to credit extended beyond said fifteen (15) day period and

not to prior extended credit nor to goods in transit received by Customer beyond said date, nor for special orders placed prior to said date notwithstanding date of delivery. Termination of this guaranty by any guarantor shall not impair the continuing guaranty of any remaining guarantor, and Creditor shall be under no obligation to notify the remaining guarantors of said termination.

Each of the undersigned warrants and represents it has full authority to enter into this guaranty.

This guaranty shall be binding upon and inure to the benefit of the parties, their successors, assigns and personal representatives.

This guaranty shall be construed and enforced under the laws of the state within which Creditor maintains its principal office.

Signed under seal this             day of          , 19    .

In the presence of:

_____     _____

_____     _____

# GUARANTY TERMINATION
## ACKNOWLEDGED

Date:

To: (Guarantor)

Re:

We acknowledge receiving your notice terminating your guaranty on the above account.

Your guarantee termination became effective as of                    , 19        .

As of said date the account owed us $                    , and you shall have a continuing obligation under your guaranty until it is fully paid.

Very truly,

_____

# NOTICE OF PURCHASE MONEY
# SECURITY INTEREST

Date:

To: (Prior Secured Parties)

Please be advised the undersigned has or expects to acquire a purchase money security interest in and to the following described collateral: (Describe)

Said collateral shall be sold to: (Debtor)

_____
Name

_____
Address

_____

Since you have an existing lien or security interest on record as against the Debtor relating to the same category of collateral (pursuant to Article 9 of the Uniform Commercial Code) this notice shall inform you of our priority claim to the property being sold. The date of sale shall be on or after                    , 19       .

Very truly,

_____

Record financing statements on property sold.

# RIGHT OF RESCISSION NOTICE

Mortgage on Property Situated at:

Mortgage Amount $

Account Number

NOTICE TO CUSTOMER OF RIGHT OF RESCISSION

AS REQUIRED BY FEDERAL LAW:

BE IT KNOWN,                                   (Customer) has entered into a

transaction on                    , 19     , which may result in a lien, mortgage

or other security interest on your home. Under federal law, you have a legal right to

cancel this transaction without any penalty or obligation within three (3) business days

from the above date or any later date on which you receive all material disclosures

required under the Truth in Lending Act. If within said three (3) day period you cancel

the transaction, any lien, mortgage, or other security interest on your home arising from

this transaction is automatically void. Further, upon cancellation within said time, you

are also entitled to receive a refund of any down payment or other consideration.

        To cancel this transaction, notify

(Name of creditor) at

(Address of creditor's place of business)

by mail or telegram sent not later than midnight of                    , 19    . Any other

form of written notice identifying the transaction may be used as a rescission notice

provided it is delivered to the creditor's place of business not later than midnight of the

date shown above. For this notice to be effective, you must date and sign below.

                                I hereby cancel this transaction.

_____        _____

(Date)                                       (Customer's Signature)

* Important Information About Your Right of Rescission on Next Page

BE IT KNOWN, receipt is acknowledged of the foregoing NOTICE, each of the undersigned **customers** having received two copies, and one copy of the Disclosure Statements concerning the above identified transaction this                     day of

                   , 19         .


_____          _____

(Customer)                                 (Customer)


EFFECT OF RESCISSION. When rescission rights are exercised under paragraph (a) of this section, a customer is not liable for any finance or other charge, and any security interest becomes void upon such a rescission. Within ten (10) days after receipt of a rescission notice, the creditor shall return to the customer any money or property given as earnest money, down payment or otherwise and shall take any action necessary or appropriate to reflect the termination of any security interest created under the transaction. If the creditor has delivered any property to the customer, the customer may retain possession of it. Upon the performance of the creditor's obligations under this section, the customer shall tender the property to the creditor, except that if return of the property in kind would be impracticable or inequitable, the customer shall tender its reasonable value. Tender shall be made at the location of the property or at the residence of the customer, at the option of the customer. If the creditor does not take possession of the property within ten (10) days after tender by the customer, ownership of the property vests in the customer without obligation on his part to pay for it.


Issue two copies to customer.

# DISCHARGE OF SECURITY INTEREST

FOR GOOD VALUE, the undersigned hereby releases, terminates and discharges a certain security interest issued by _____ (Debtor) to the undersigned dated _____ , 19 ____ , represented by filing no. _____ .

This document _____ shall, _____ ; shall not _____ (check one) constitute a discharge of any obligation for which said security interest was granted.

We shall further execute such terminations of financing statements of public record as may be requested by the debtor.

Signed under seal this _____ day of _____ , 19 ____ .

Witnessed:

_____     _____
                             Secured Party

# PLEDGE OF PROPERTY

FOR GOOD VALUE, the undersigned deposits and pledges with

(Pledgee) as collateral security to secure the

payment of the following debts:

The property (collateral) described as:

Pursuant to this pledge the following is also agreed:

• (Pledgee) may assign or transfer said debt and the pledged

collateral hereunder.

• (Pledgee) shall have no liability for loss, destruction or casualty

to the collateral unless caused by pledgee's own negligence.

• The undersigned shall pay all insurance it elects to maintain or

(Pledgee) reasonably requires on the pledged collateral and shall pay any property,

excise or other tax or levy.

• The undersigned warrants and represents that good title is had to the property

being pledged, full authority to pledge said property is maintained, and that the pledged

property is free of any adverse liens, encumbrances, adverse claims or prior pledge.

• Upon default of or breach of this pledge agreement,

(Pledgee) or holder may foreclose on the pledged collateral and exercise its rights as a

secured party pursuant to Article 9 of the Uniform Commercial Code; said rights being

cumulative with any other rights (Pledgee) may have

against the undersigned.

• Upon foreclosure the pledged property may be sold at either public auction or private sale, and the undersigned shall be given reasonable notice of the intended sale; the undersigned may redeem said property at any time before said sale upon payment of the balance due.

• Upon payment of the obligation for which the property is pledged, the property shall be returned to the undersigned, and this pledge agreement shall be terminated.

• This pledge agreement shall be binding upon and inure to the benefit of the parties, their successors, assigns, personal agents and representatives.

• Upon default the undersigned shall pay all reasonable attorneys' fees and costs of collection.

Signed under seal this          day of          , 19     .

_____     _____

Pledgee

_____     _____

Pledgor (undersigned)

# NOTICE OF DEFAULT
# ON PROMISSORY NOTE

Date:

To:

REFERENCE:  Promissory note dated                              , 19      , in the
original amount of $                              .

The payment due on                              , 19      , for $
has not been paid. Consequently, you are now in default on the said note.

Please pay the amount due within the next seven days.

If payment is not made within the specified period, we shall proceed to enforce
our rights to collect the entire balance.

Cordially,

_____

# DEMAND FOR PAYMENT
# ON PROMISSORY NOTE

Date:

To:

    I refer to your promissory note dated ·                  , 19     , in the original principal amount of $              to which the undersigned is holder.

    You are in default on this note because the following payment(s) have not made been made.

         __Payment Date__                      __Amount Due__

    Accordingly, demand is made for full payment of the entire balance of $                   due under the note. If payment is not received within         days, this note shall be turned over to our attorneys for collection, and you shall be responsible for all reasonable costs of collection.

    Very truly,

_____

# DEMAND FOR PAYMENT
# ON GUARANTOR


Date:


To:



The undersigned holds your guaranty dated                          , 19       ,

wherein you guarantee the debt owed us by




Please be advised that said obligation is in default. Demand is made upon you as

a guarantor for full payment on the outstanding debt now due us in the amount of

$                                    .

If payment is not made within                          days, we shall enforce our

rights against you under the guaranty and hold you responsible for attorney's fees and

costs of collection.


Very truly,


_____

# DEMAND FOR PAYMENT
## ON ENDORSERS

Date:

To:

(Undersigned) holds the below described (check) (note)
to which you are an endorser:

Maker

Date

Original Amount

You are advised that said instrument has not been paid, and demand is hereby
made upon you to immediately pay the following amount due in the sum of

$                    .

If you fail to make payment within five (5) days from the date this demand is
received,                    (Undersigned) shall take legal action to enforce your
warranties of endorsement.

Upon payment, we shall assign to you such rights as we have to the instrument.

Cordially,

_____

# DEMAND BY SECURED PARTY
# FOR REPOSSESSION OF COLLATERAL

Date:

To: (Debtor)

I refer to a security agreement granted to us on                    ,

19    .

I advise you that you are in default of said security agreement because:

Accordingly, demand is made for the surrender and delivery to us of all the

collateral under said security agreement described as:

We intend to exercise our rights of foreclosure and sale pursuant to the Uniform

Commercial Code.

Very truly,

_____

# SURRENDER OF COLLATERAL

BE IT ACKNOWLEDGED, that the undersigned (Debtor) to a security agreement dated _____, 19___, granted to _____ (Secured Party) acknowledges:

1.      The Debtor presently owes Secured Party $_____ and that confession of judgment may be entered for said amount.

2.      Debtor has defaulted on his obligations to Secured Party and that Secured Party has the rights of foreclosure under its security agreements.

3.      In lieu of foreclosure by Secured Party, Debtor delivers, assigns and surrenders to Secured Party all collateral under the security agreement.

4.      Debtor hereby waives all rights to redeem said collateral and assents to any commercially reasonable public or private sale of said collateral.

5.      Debtor waives all notices of foreclosure or public or private sale as required under the security agreement or Uniform Commercial Code.

6.      Upon sale, the Secured Party shall render to Debtor an accounting of proceeds plus expenses and remit any surplus.

7.      Debtor shall remain liable for any deficiency from sale of the collateral, including payment of costs of foreclosure and reasonable attorney's fees.


Signed under seal this _____ day of _____, 19___ .


Witnessed:      _____


Debtor:      _____

# NOTICE OF PUBLIC SALE
# OF COLLATERAL

Date:

To: (Debtor)

You are provided notice that the collateral covered under our security agreement shall be sold at public auction as follows:

Date:

Time:

Location:

You will be held liable for any deficiency resulting from said sale.

You may redeem the collateral by paying the amount due plus accrued costs of foreclosure at any time prior to the time of sale. You shall have no right to redeem the property after the sale. The balance as of this date, including costs is

$                                        . All payments must be by certified or bank check.

_____

Certified Mail

# NOTICE OF PRIVATE SALE
## OF COLLATERAL

Date:

To: (Debtor)

You are notified that on                          , 19      , the undersigned, as

secured party-in-possession, shall sell at private sale the following collateral:

Said collateral shall be sold to                                        (Buyer) for

$                          .

You will be held liable for any deficiency resulting from said sale.

You may redeem this collateral by paying the amount due plus accrued costs of

foreclosure at any time prior to the time of sale. You shall have no right to redeem the

property after the sale. The balance due as of this date (including accrued interest and

costs) is $                          . All payments must be by certified or bank

check.

_____

Certified Mail

# NOTICE TO SUBORDINATE LIENHOLDER
# OF FORECLOSURE AND INTENDED SALE

Date:

To:

The Undersigned is a lienholder against certain assets owned by

, currently indebted to us in the amount of

$                        .

The Undersigned, as lienholder-in-possession of said collateral, intends to sell the following collateral towards satisfaction of this debt:

Said sale shall be by public auction

     Date:

     Time:

     Location:

– or by private sale

     Date:

     Time:

     Buyer:

     Price:

Since you hold a subordinate security interest or lien, you are provided the statutory notice of said intended sale.

Very truly,

_____

# Credit and Collections

# CREDIT INFORMATION REQUEST

Date:

To: (Customer)

We appreciate your recent order and would be pleased to consider you for a line of credit, however, we need further information to grant credit.

Would you please provide us with the information checked?

_____    Your Bank(s)

_____    Credit Application (enclosed)

_____    Current Financial Statements

_____    (        ) Trade References and a Bank Reference

_____    Dun and Bradstreet or Other Credit Reporting Rating

_____    Other:

Until we receive this information, we recommend C.O.D. or advance payment of $ on this order. This will help avoid delay in shipment. Upon receipt we shall immediately ship.

A self-addressed return envelope is enclosed for your convenience. Of course, all credit information shall be held in strict confidence.

Very truly,

_____

# REQUEST FOR BANK CREDIT REFERENCE

Date:

To: (Bank)

Re:

The above captioned suggested we contact you for a banking reference. We would appreciate the following information:

1.   How long has the account had a banking relationship with you?

2.   What is the average account balance?

3.   Does the account routinely overdraft?

4.   Is the account a borrowing or non-borrowing account?

5.   If the account borrows, please advise as to:

     Present balance on secured loans        $

     Present balance on unsecured loans      $

     Terms of repayment:

     Is repayment satisfactory?

6.   Is the banking relationship generally satisfactory?

Other comments or information would be greatly appreciated and shall be held in the strictest confidence. We certainly would be pleased to reciprocate.

_____

# REQUEST FOR CREDIT HISTORY

Date:

To: (Trade References)

Re: (Account Name)

BE IT KNOWN, the above has applied to us for credit and has listed you as a credit reference. Please be kind enough to provide us the benefit of your credit experience with the account by furnishing the following information:

Highest credit balance

Lowest credit balance

Terms

Credit furnished to account since

Current balance

Credit limit

Payment history

Use the reverse side to note other credit comments. This information shall be held strictly confidential. We are always pleased to reciprocate.

Cordially,

_____

# CREDIT REFERENCE ACKNOWLEDGEMENT

Date:

To: (Credit Reference)

Re: (Account)

We have received your credit information on the above customer.

Your cooperation in providing this information is appreciated and is valuable to our effort to establish an appropriate credit level for the account.

Should you see a need to change your credit policy with the account or find a change in the account's financial condition that may be of interest to us, we would also appreciate receipt of this information.

We will certainly hold all information strictly confidential and, of course, will reciprocate the courtesy at any time.

We thank you for your courtesy.

Very truly,

_____

# CREDIT HISTORY TRANSMITTAL

Date:

To:

Re: (Account)

We reply to your request for credit information on the above account and submit
the following information:

1.      We have sold the account since                                      .

2.      The account's present balance is:

                Under 30 days  $

                30-60 days      $

                60-90 Days      $

                Over 90 days    $

                Total owed:      $

3.      We currently sell the account on the following credit terms:


4.      Other credit information:



We trust this information shall be held in strict confidence.


Cordially,


_____

# PARTIAL SHIPMENT REQUEST

Date:

To: (Customer)

      We appreciate your order dated                 , 19     . The order is for approximately $           , however, we regret we cannot extend you credit for the entire order at the present time.

      We suggest we ship you on our standard credit terms a partial shipment for $        . Upon receiving payment we shall release the balance of the order. If you want a different order configuration please advise.

      Unless we hear from you to the contrary within the next ten (10) days, we shall ·ip on these terms.

Very truly,

_____

# NOTICE OF C.O.D. TERMS

Date:

To: (Customer)

We appreciate your order dated            , 19    , (or as attached) and your request for credit terms.

While we want to accept your order, we unfortunately cannot ship on credit terms at the present time.

Accordingly, we propose to ship to you C.O.D. unless we are notified of the contrary within ten (10) days.

Thank you for your understanding and patronage.

Very truly,

_____

# AGREEMENT TO APPLY
# TRADE ALLOWANCES

Date:

To: (Customer)

      This will confirm our understanding that we shall apply all future trade discounts, advertising and promotional allowances or rebates, and other customary concessions to your outstanding balance. We also expect your payments toward your account as per our payment agreement.

      We hope this arrangement will assist us both in liquidating your balance.

Very truly,

_____

# NOTICE OF UNPAID INVOICE

Date:

To: (Customer)

We received on                                    , 19        , your check for

$                paying the following invoice(s):

        <u>Invoice(s)</u>             <u>Amount</u>

Your payment did not pay the following invoice(s) which are now overdue.

        <u>Invoice(s)</u>             <u>Amount</u>

We assume the unpaid invoice(s) are due to oversight. Please let us know if you need copies of the unpaid invoice(s) or if you question these invoice(s), otherwise we shall expect payment on these outstanding invoices for $                .

We appreciate your prompt attention to this matter.

Very truly,

_____

# DISCOUNT DISALLOWED NOTICE

Date:

To: (Customer)

Thank you for your payment for $ _____ for the following invoice(s).

### Invoice(s)

Your payment includes an unearned discount of $ _____ which we cannot grant since your payment was received _____ days beyond the cash discount date.

To adjust your account we shall:

_____ Apply the checks to the invoice balances but debit your account the $ _____ unearned discount.

_____ Return your check and request that you issue us a new check for $ _____ .

_____ Have our sales representative arrange to exchange these checks for new checks.

We regret we cannot allow you the unearned discount, but, in fairness to all our customers we must strictly adhere to our discount policy.

Very truly,

_____

# PAYMENT INQUIRY

Date:

To: (Customer)

We don't understand why your account balance of $                    has not been paid.

Take a moment and help resolve it, and let us know where we stand.

1.    The account has not been paid because


2.    The account will be paid on or before                    , 19    .

3.    Check is enclosed.


Your reply is appreciated.


Very truly,

_____

# SECOND NOTICE
# OF OVERDUE ACCOUNT

Date:

To: (Customer)

There's no better way to show you why we are concerned about your overdue payment than to show you your account balance.

## PAST DUE

Over 30 days                                   $_____

Over 60 days                                   $_____

Over 90 days                                   $_____

                          Total due            $_____

May we <u>now</u> have your check?

Very truly,

_____

# DEMAND FOR PAYMENT

Date:

To: (Customer)

      Although we have tried to resolve your past due account, the problem continues. Your account remains seriously overdue in the amount of $         .

      This is your final notice. Unless we have your check for $          within the next ten (10) days, we shall immediately turn your account over for collection.

      Immediate payment is in your own best interest as it will save you added interest and court costs and help protect your credit rating.

Very truly,

_____

# FINAL COLLECTION NOTICE PRIOR TO
# LEGAL ACTION

Date:

To:  (The Debtor)

Re:  (Account Number)

We have repeatedly asked for your long overdue payment in the amount of

$                    . Unless we receive a certified or cashier's check for such

amount by            , 199  , we will turn your account over to our attorneys with

instructions to institute a suit for collection of your account without further delay.

There is still time to avoid suit if you contact us within the next five (5) days

from the date this notice is received .

This is your final opportunity to resolve matters without the expense of court

proceedings. Keep in mind that referral of your account to attorneys is likely to impair

your credit rating.

Cordially,

_____

# REQUEST FOR INFORMATION
## ON DISPUTED CHARGE

Date:

To: (Customer)

Reference is made to your claim disputing certain charges on your account for the following reason(s):

To respond to your claim, we need the following (circled) information or documents:

Copies of invoices noted on attached sheet.

Copies of cancelled checks.

Credit memos.

Return goods authorizations.

List of items claimed as not received.

List of items claimed non-conforming.

Other: _____

Thank you for your prompt attention. Once you send us the circled documents, we shall resolve this matter as promptly as possible.

Cordially,

_____

# SETTLEMENT OFFER
# ON DISPUTED ACCOUNT

Date:

To: (Creditor)

We have received your statements or claim for $                    .

We contest the claimed balance for the following reasons:

Without prejudice or admission of liability, but as an offer of compromise only, we propose to settle this by paying $                    . Our check for this sum is enclosed. Deposit of the check shall discharge the entire balance claimed, pursuant to the release endorsement. If this is not acceptable, please return the check immediately.

Very truly,

_____

# INSTALLMENT PAYMENT
# ACKNOWLEDGEMENT

Date:

To: (Customer)

We are glad to resolve your overdue balance by accepting your agreement to pay us the $_____ balance owed us in _____ payments of $_____ each. We look forward to your first payment on _____, 19___, as per your agreement.

If any payment is missed, we shall have no alternative but to collect the entire balance then due. But we have every confidence that this action will not be necessary.

Your future business is greatly appreciated.

Very truly,

_____

Acknowledged:

_____

# CONFIRMATION OF
# PAYMENT PLAN

Date:

To: (Customer)

We are glad we could reach payment agreement on your overdue balance of

$                          .

To confirm our understanding, you shall pay the balance as follows:



We understand your financial difficulties and will accept payments on the above terms provided the payments are punctually made when due.

While you have an outstanding balance we shall ship on a C.O.D. basis and, of course, grant to you all cash discounts on your purchases.

If this does not conform to our understanding, please advise at once.

I am pleased this matter could be resolved on terms satisfactory to us both, and we look forward to both your payments and continued patronage.

Very truly,

_____

The above is acknowledged:

_____

Customer

# NOTICE OF DEFAULT
# ON EXTENSION AGREEMENT


Date:

To: (Customer)



      I refer to your payment agreement dated              , 19    . You agreed to pay $           each (week/month) on your overdue account.

      Your payment due            , 19    , for $      has not been received. If this was due to an oversight, please send payment within the next ten (10) days, and we shall reinstate the agreement.

      If payment is not made, we shall immediately enforce our rights to collect the balance of $        .


               Very truly,


_____

# CREDITOR'S AFFIDAVIT

        I, _____ of _____ , the Undersigned, being of age, do of my own personal knowledge make the following statements and declare them to be true.

1.      I am _____ of _____ , Plaintiff in this action and have custody of its books and records.

2.      According to said books and records and my own personal knowledge, Defendant owes Plaintiff the amount of $ _____ without setoff defense or counterclaim.

3.      Notwithstanding repeated demand for payment, no payment has been received.

4.      There is no insurance coverage or other posted security from which to satisfy this claim.

        Signed under penalty of perjury this _____ day of _____ , 19 ____ .

_____

State of _____

County of _____ , 19 ____ .

        Then personally appeared _____ who executed the foregoing affidavit before me.

_____

Notary Public

# TURNOVER FOR COLLECTION

Date:

To: (Attorney or Collection Agency)

Re:   (Account)

Amount due: $

We place for collection the above claim, and

To assist you in your collection efforts enclose:

_____   Our complete file

_____   Account ledgers

_____   Outstanding invoices

_____   Affidavit of amount due

_____   Notes/security agreements/loan documents

_____   Correspondence

_____   Guarantees/indemnities

_____   Credit application

_____   Other: (Describe)

_____   Court fees $

We also provide you the following information:

1.      Customer's stated reason for non-payment.

2.      Prior payment agreements.

3.    Customer's financial condition.


4.    Defenses or counterclaims that customer may assert.


5.    Other creditors owed.


6.    Other.


Thank you for your efforts on this matter.


                                          _____

# DEBT ACKNOWLEDGEMENT

The Undersigned debtor confirms to                    (Creditor) that the Undersigned owes Creditor $                    as of this date, which amount includes all accrued interest and other permitted charges to date. We further agree there are no defenses, credits or rights of setoff and that the Creditor may enter a confession of judgment (where so allowed by law) against the Undersigned for the amount acknowledged to be due.

Signed under seal this                    day of                    , 19        .

Witness:

_____        _____

_____

# ASSENT AND PROOF OF CLAIM

The Undersigned creditor assents to the terms of a certain (assignment/trust mortgage) entered into by _____ (account) to _____ (assignee/trust). We do become a party to said instrument as an assenting creditor and, in accordance with said instrument, agree to accept in full payment of all debts, claims and demands the dividends or creditor distribution payable under said instrument and do release, acquit and discharge the debtor from all other debts, claims and demands.

Witness our hand and seal this _____ day of _____ , 19 ____ .

Creditor

By: _____

Duly Authorized

Creditor's Name: _____

Creditor's Address: _____

_____

Amount of Claim:  $ _____

ATTACH COPY OF STATEMENT

# DEBT REAFFIRMATION

FOR GOOD AND VALUABLE CONSIDERATION RECEIVED, the

Undersigned affirms to

(Creditor) and its successors and assigns a prior, released, extinguished or canceled debt

for $               . The Undersigned shall remain bound on said debt in the

amount of $               and to the same extent as if said debt to the amount

stated were not discharged in the first instance.

I further agree that the above reaffirmed debt shall be paid as follows:



In addition, if said debt was discharged under any provision of the United States

Bankruptcy Code, then this reaffirmation shall be subject to approval by the United

States Bankruptcy Court, and the Undersigned shall diligently apply for said approval.

This agreement shall be binding upon the parties, their successors , assigns and

personal representatives.


Signed under seal this               day of               , 19       .


Witness:


_____          _____

                                         Debtor

# AUTHORIZATION TO RELEASE
# CREDIT INFORMATION

Date:

To:

    Creditor

    I have credit with your firm and request that my credit history be forwarded to the credit reporting agencies listed below. This letter is my authorization to release this information.

Credit Reporting Agencies:        Agency Addresses:

_____     _____

_____     _____

_____     _____

_____     _____

_____     _____

Name of Account             Account Number

_____     _____

Signature              Signature of Joint Applicant (if any)

# ADVERSE CREDIT
# INFORMATION REQUEST


Date:

To:

      Creditor


      You have declined me credit. I hereby ask you to disclose the reasons for this credit denial and for any adverse credit information about me that you have received from any source other than a consumer reporting agency, including the identity of such source.

_____

Signature                                  Print Name

_____

Credit Application Date                  Address

_____

Transaction or Type Credit               Telephone Number

                                       _____

                                       Prior or Other Addresses

State of

County of                                              , 19   .

      Then personally appeared                          who acknowledged the foregoing before me.


                                        _____

                                       Notary Public

                                        My Commission Expires:

# Buying/Selling Goods

# VERBAL ORDER CONFIRMATION

Date:

To: (Supplier)

BE IT KNOWN, this confirms your acceptance of our verbal order of

(Description of order), on

, 19     .

A confirming purchase order containing the stated terms is enclosed as purchase order no.          .

Unless we receive a written objection from you within ten (10) days of your receipt of this order, the order will be deemed confirmed on its terms, and we shall anticipate delivery of all ordered goods on the date stated.

Thank you for your cooperation.

Cordially,

_____

# PURCHASE ORDER EXCEPTIONS

Date:

To:

We have received your purchase order no.           , dated

      , 19   .

We confirm acceptance of said order subject only to the following exceptions:
(Describe)

We shall assume you agree to the exceptions noted unless objection is received within ten (10) days of your receipt of this notice. We shall promptly ship goods not subject to exception.

Thank you for your business, and we trust you understand the reasons for the exception.

Very truly,

_____

# ACKNOWLEDGEMENT OF MODIFICATION
# OF CONTRACT TERMS

                                    Date:

To:

Re:  Modified Contract Terms

        BE IT KNOWN, that the contract or order between

and                          dated                     , 19     , as annexed

herewith, has been modified as of                      , 19    .

        This letter acknowledges that the contract or order is modified and superseded

by the following terms:

        All other terms remain as stated.

        Unless you notify me otherwise, in writing, we shall consider said modification

to be mutually agreeable as of date stated above and shall proceed on the modified terms.

                                    Cordially,

                        _____

# DEMAND FOR ACKNOWLEDGEMENT
## OF SHIPPING DATES

Date:

To: (Supplier)

Please confirm and specify shipping arrangements on our order of

, 19    . Also furnish us timely assurance that you shall comply with its

terms.

Failure to assure shall constitute a breach of said contract, and we shall no longer

consider ourselves obligated to perform under said contract. We shall then hold you

responsible for all damages pursuant to the Uniform Commercial Code.

Very truly,

_____

# DEMAND FOR DELIVERY

Date:

To: (Supplier)


      The Undersigned has paid you $                  for goods to be shipped

pursuant to our accepted order dated              , 19    ; and we

therefore demand delivery of said goods in accordance with our order.

      Unless these goods are received by us on or before            ,

19    , we shall consider you in breach and demand full refund, reserving all other

rights under the Uniform Commercial Code.

      Please notify us of your intentions.


                      Very truly,


                      _____

# NOTICE OF REFUSAL
## TO ACCEPT DELIVERY

Date:

To:

    We refer to your order dated                , 19   , a copy of which is attached.

    Because of your wrongful refusal to accept delivery of said goods under the purchase contract, we shall not attempt further shipment, and we hold you liable for all damages arising from your failure to fulfill your obligations under the order.

    Should you have any questions on this matter, please call us immediately.

Very truly,

_____

# NOTICE OF REJECTION OF GOODS

Date:

To:

We received goods from you under our order or contract dated                    ,

19          . However, we reject said goods for the reason(s) circled below:

Goods failed to be delivered within the required contract time.

Goods were defective or damaged as described on attached sheet.

Goods did not conform to sample or specifications as described on attached sheet.

Confirmation accepting our order, as required, has not been received, and we therefore

ordered the goods from another supplier.

Prices for said goods do not conform to quote, catalogue or purchase order price.

Partial shipment only received; we do not accept partial shipments.

Other (see attached sheet).

Please provide instructions for return of said goods at your expense. Rejection of

said goods shall not waive any other claim we may have.

Cordially,

_____

# NOTICE OF CANCELLATION OF
# BACK-ORDERED GOODS

Date:

To:

BE IT KNOWN, that pursuant to our purchase order dated

, 19        as attached, we have received only a partial shipment. As noted by you

on the packing invoice, some goods are out of stock or back ordered.

Please be advised that we are cancelling the back-ordered goods. Invoice us only

for the goods received. If the back-ordered goods are in transit, please advise at once and

we shall give you further instructions.

Cordially,

_____

# NOTICE TO CANCEL ORDER
# DUE TO DELAYED SHIPMENT

Date:

To:

I refer to our purchase order or contract dated                                        ,
19        , as attached.

Under said order, the goods were to be shipped by                                      ,
19        .

Because you failed to ship the goods within the required time, we cancel the order and reserve such further rights and remedies as we may have, including damage claims under the Uniform Commercial Code.

If said goods are in transit, they shall be refused and returned at your expense under your shipping instructions.

Very truly,

_____

# NOTIFICATION OF
# NONCONFORMING GOODS

Date:

To: (Supplier)

Please be advised that on                         , 19   , we received the goods

that you shipped to us pursuant to invoice number(s)                      .

BE IT KNOWN, that we have inspected said goods some of which do not

conform to specification or sample for the following reasons:

Accordingly, we reject said nonconforming goods and request a credit for

$                              . We further request return shipping instructions.

You are advised that we reserve such further rights as provided under the

Uniform Commercial Code.

Cordially,

_____

# NOTICE TO SELLER
# OF DEFECTIVE GOODS

Date:

To:

We have inspected goods shipped to us pursuant to your invoice or order number

_____ , dated _____ , 19 _____ .

Pleased be advised that the goods listed below are defective for the following

reasons:

Item(s):                              Defect(s):

_____             _____

_____             _____

_____             _____

In light of non-conformity, we reject said goods, and request credit or adjustment

in the amount of $ _____ which represents the billed amount. As is

customary, we intend to re-ship these goods to you at your expense.

Upon receipt of this notice, please confirm the credit and provide instructions for

re-shipment of said goods.

Be advised that we reserve such further rights as we may have under the

Uniform Commercial Code.

Cordially,

_____

# ACCEPTANCE OF DAMAGED GOODS

Date:

To:

      We have received the following defective or non-conforming goods on our order

dated                    , 19 .

      We shall accept said goods if we are granted a price reduction of

$                .

      Please advise of your acceptance of these terms immediately, or we shall be

required to return said goods at your expense, reserving such rights and remedies as we

have under the Uniform Commercial Code.

                                   Very truly,

                            _____

# CONFIRMATION OF
# GOODS RECEIVED

Date:

Please be advised that                                    (Undersigned) received
goods from                              (Supplier) on                          ,
19    . The goods are identified by invoice/shipping or packing slip no.                , or
Bill of Lading no.                          .

We have been provided full opportunity to inspect said goods. Said goods have
been received in good condition, free of defects or damage and in full conformity to our
order with no items missing or short except as may be specifically noted below.

Cordially,

_____

Items (if any) damaged or short

# SALE ON APPROVAL
# ACKNOWLEDGEMENT

Date:

To: (Customer)

We acknowledge shipment of the goods delivered on the attached invoice or order on a <u>sale on approval</u> basis.

Please be advised that if you are not satisfied with the goods, you have the right to return all or any part thereof at our expense within _____ days of receipt for full credit (or refund if prepaid). However, if you fail to return goods within the time stated above, you shall be deemed to have accepted said goods, and there shall be no further right of return.

We appreciate your business and trust that the quality of our goods will meet with your approval.

Cordially,

_____

# NOTICE OF
# WITHHELD DELIVERY

Date:

To: (Customer)

       I refer to your order dated                    , 19    , on your purchase order no.              .

       We must withhold delivery for the below reason(s)

  _____  Overdue balance of \$          .

  _____  You canceled this order.

  _____  Certain items are back-ordered and shipment will be made in single lot.

  _____  Other (Describe)

       Please respond so we may fulfill your order without further delay or inconvenience.

                        Very truly,

_____

# ACCEPTANCE OF ORDER
## WITH DELIVERY IN LOTS

Date:

To: (Customer)

We accept your order of                        , 19      . The goods will be

shipped to you as follows:

We request payment as each lot is received, and delivery of each subsequent lot

shall be expressly conditional upon the prompt payment on prior lots.

We hope these terms are acceptable. Unless notified to the contrary, we shall

ship on the stated terms.

Very truly,

_____

# NOTICE OF
# PRODUCT DEFECT CLAIM

Date:

To:

We have sold a product manufactured by you described as:

We have been advised by our customer of a product defect or warranty claim as follows:

Name of Customer:

Date of Purchase:

Nature of Claimed Defect:

Injuries or Damage Claimed:

If suit or claim is brought against us for breach of warranty of merchantability (or any such similar claim), we shall seek full reimbursement and indemnification from you.

This letter gives you the earliest possible notice of a potential claim.

We shall advise you upon receipt of any further information on this claim.

Very truly,

_____

# NOTICE OF RESALE

Date:

To: (Customer)

I refer to your purchase order/invoice annexed:

You breached your purchase contract because:

Accordingly, I notify you that said items shall be resold at public auction as follows:

Date:

Place:

Time:

Pursuant to the Uniform Commercial Code, you shall be held liable for any difference between your contract price and the price at which the goods are resold, together with the costs and expense of resale.

Very truly,

_____

# NOTICE TO STOP GOODS
# IN TRANSIT

Date:

To:  (Common Carrier)

Please be advised that you received goods sent by us on                      ,

19    , to be shipped by you for delivery to:

_____

_____

_____

\* Shipping documents enclosed.

Please stop transit of said goods, do not make delivery to the consignee, and

return said goods to us. We shall pay return freight charges. Goods may not be delivered.

No negotiable bill of lading or document of title has been delivered to our

customer (consignee).

Cordially,

_____

Copy to:

_____

Customer

# NOTICE TO
# RECLAIM GOODS


Date:

To: (Customer)


    We shipped you certain goods within the past ten (10) days as represented by the attached invoices.

    It has come to our attention that your firm is insolvent, and pursuant to the Uniform Commercial Code, demand return and reclamation of these goods.

    If the goods have been sold, this notice shall constitute a priority claim for the value of said goods not available for return; demand is made for the return of any goods still within your possession.


    Very truly,


_____

# AUTHORIZATION TO
# RETURN GOODS

Date:

To: (Customer)

Please allow this letter to acknowledge that we shall accept certain return goods for credit. The terms for return are:

1.      The aggregate cost value of the goods subject to return shall not exceed

$                              .

2.      We shall deduct                    % of the cost price as handling charges to process the return goods, crediting the balance to your account.

3.      All return goods shall be in resaleable condition and represent goods we either currently stock or can return to our suppliers for credit. As a result, we reserve the right to reject nonconforming goods.

4.      Return goods must be invoiced and are subject to inspection and return approval before shipment to us.

5.      If goods are shipped via common carrier, you shall be responsible for all freight costs and risk of loss in transit. Goods shall not be considered accepted for return until we have received, inspected and approved said goods at our place of business.

6.      Our agreement to accept returns for credit is expressly conditional upon your agreement to pay any remaining balance due on the following terms:

You understand this return privilege is extended only to resolve your account balance and is not necessarily standing policy. Thank you for your cooperation in this matter.

Very truly,

_____

# Leases and Tenancies

# LEASE

LEASE between                                          (Landlord) and

                                   (Tenant).

For good consideration it is agreed that

(Landlord) leases to                                   (Tenant) the premises

located at                                             (Address).

This Lease shall be for a term of              years commencing on

                , 19        , and terminating on                        , 19        .

Pursuant to said lease agreement,                              (Tenant) shall

pay                              (Landlord) an annual rent of $

during said term, in monthly payments of $                    each, payable monthly

in advance. Tenant shall also pay a security deposit of $                   , due upon

execution of said lease agreement.

                              (Tenant) shall be obligated to pay for the

following utilities:


                              (Landlord) shall be obligated to pay for the

following utilities:




                                   (Tenant) further agrees that upon the

lease expiration, said premises will be returned to its present condition, reasonable wear

and tear and fire casualty excepted, and also agrees not to commit waste to the leased

premises.

Furthermore,                                   (Tenant) agrees not to assign

nor sublet said premises nor allow any other person to occupy the leased premises without                              (Landlord's) prior approval with written

consent.

Finally,                          (Tenant) agrees not to make any

material or structural alterations to the leased premises without

(Landlord's) prior approval with written consent.

# LEASE EXTENSION AGREEMENT

Date

(Landlord) and

(Tenant) agree to extend lease on said premises known as

(Address and Describe), original lease

dated                , 19     (Lease.)

For good consideration                          (Landlord) and

(Tenant) agree to extend the said lease term for a period

of            years, starting date                          , 19        , and

terminating date                              , 19    . The parties agree that no further

right of renewal or extension shall exist beyond termination date indicated above.

During the lease extension period,

(Tenant) agrees to pay rent of $                    per annum, payable $

per month in advance. Other terms modified by this lease extension agreement include

the following (describe):


All other lease terms shall remain unchanged and continue during the lease

extension period as is set forth herein.

This agreement shall be binding upon and shall inure to the benefit of the parties,

their successors, assigns, personal agents and representatives.

_____          _____

(Landlord)                               (Date)

_____          _____

(Tenant)                                 (Date)

_____          _____

(Witness)                                (Date)

# AGREEMENT TO TERMINATE LEASE

Date

FOR GOOD CONSIDERATION,

(Landlord) and                                        (Tenant) as of

(Date) hereby mutually agree to terminate and cancel said lease dated

, 19    , on premises known as


(Address and Describe). Both                                        (Landlord) and

(Tenant) hereby agree that this termination agreement

cancels all rights and obligations under said lease excepting only for any unpaid rent

obligations accruing under the lease prior to the effective termination date.

(Tenant) agrees to promptly surrender the premises by

the termination date and to return said premises to

(Landlord) in the same condition received to the extent reasonably possible, free

of                                        (Tenant's) goods and effects.

This agreement shall be binding upon the parties, their successors, assigns,

personal agents and representatives.

_____          _____

(Tenant)                                               (Date)

_____          _____

(Landlord)                                            (Date)

_____          _____

(Witness)                                             (Date)

# SUBLEASE AGREEMENT

1.      This sublease is between

(Tenant) and                                                          (Subtenant).

2.      Pursuant to said sublease agreement,

(Subtenant) hereby agrees to lease the following premises at

(Address and Describe)

commencing on                                    , 19      , and terminating on

                        , 19      .

3.                                          (Subtenant) agrees to abide by all terms

and conditions of original lease entered into by

(Tenant) and                                      (Landlord) on

              , 19      . The original lease agreement and all terms and conditions

thereof is hereby incorporated by reference into said sublease agreement.

                        (Subtenant) agrees to pay

(Landlord) the monthly rent stated in the original lease, which is $                          .

4.                                      (Subtenant) agrees to pay

                        (Tenant) a security deposit in the sum of $

due upon the signing of said sublease agreement. Said deposit shall be returned to

                        (Subtenant) provided said premises are returned to

                        (Tenant) in the same condition received, to the extent

reasonably possible.

5.      Inventory of items that were in the above-described property on

              , 19      , includes the following:

_____    _____

_____    _____

_____    _____

If any items are missing or damaged, _____ (Subtenant) hereby

agrees to replace or reimburse said items for _____

(Tenant).

6. _____ (Landlord) hereby grants permission to this

sublease and agrees to promptly notify _____ (Tenant) at

_____ (Address and Phone Number) if

_____ (Subtenant) defaults in this agreement. Nothing herein shall constitute a

release of _____ (Tenant) who shall remain bound and wholly

liable under all terms and conditions of this lease.


_____    _____

(Landlord)                       (Date)

_____    _____

(Tenant)                         (Date)

_____    _____

(Subtenant)                      (Date)

# LEASE ASSIGNMENT

BE IT KNOWN THAT,                                    (Assignor) for

valued consideration agrees and hereby assigns to

(Assignee) all of                                    (Assignor's) remaining rights in

and to a certain lease made by                                    (Assignor) and

                                    (Landlord) for premises described as

pursuant to lease dated                                    , 19      .

                                    (Assignee) agrees to fully perform all of

                                    (Assignor's) obligations under said Lease after delivery

of possession thereto.

Pursuant to said assignment,                                    (Assignor)

agrees and shall deliver possession of the leased premises to

(Assignee) no later than                                    , 19      (Effective Date).

Pursuant to said assignment between                                    (Assignor)

and                                    (Assignee),                                    (Landlord)

hereby consents to said lease assignment.

All parties acknowledge said lease to be in good standing and in full force

without modification.

This agreement shall be binding upon and inure to the benefit of the parties, their

successors, assigns, personal agents, and representatives.

_____          _____

(Assignor)                                              (Date)

_____          _____

(Assignee)                                              (Date)

_____          _____

(Landlord)                                              (Date)

# NOTICE TO EXERCISE

# LEASE OPTION

Date:

To: (Lessor)


       This exercise of lease option pertains to said lease between

                   (Lessor) and                        (Lessee)

dated              , 19    , for the following premises:


(Description and Address).

       Under the terms of the lease, we have the option for an extension or renewal for

a year term commencing on              , 19   .

       By this notice, we advise you of our intent to exercise the option to renew/extend

(circle one) the lease on the terms agreed to.


                            _____

                            Lessee

# LANDLORD'S WAIVER
# TO TENANT'S FIXTURES

BE IT KNOWN,                                  (Landlord) hereby waives all claim to certain equipment, fixtures, improvements, accessories or appurtenances as may be installed by                             (Tenant) on the premises at                                             .

                                    (Landlord) agrees that said personal property are trade fixtures and shall remain property of                         (Tenant) and may be removed by                          (Tenant) when the tenancy expires. However, pursuant to this waiver                     (Tenant) agrees to restore said premises to its original condition to the extent reasonably practicable.

This agreement shall be binding upon and inure to the benefit of the parties, their successors, assigns, personal agents, and representatives.

Signed under seal this                    day of                 , 19     .

In the presence of:

_____
Landlord


_____    _____
                                                    Tenant

# TENANT'S NOTICE
# TERMINATING TENANCY


Date:

To: (Landlord)


As your tenant occupying the premises known as:



We advise you of our intention to terminate our tenancy on or before

                , 19     , and to deliver to you full possession of the

premises.


_____

(Tenant)

# LEGAL VACATE NOTICE

Date:

To                                                   (Tenant or Subtenant),
and all other persons who now occupy said premises known as

(Address and Describe).

(Landlord) is hereby giving you
notice to vacate said premises described above which are now being occupied by you.

You are hereby ordered to deliver possession of said premises to
(Landlord) on or before          , 19   .

This legal notice is a result of your breach of tenancy, namely:

Unless said breach is cured by               , 19   (Date), you must
vacate said premises within           days from receipt of this notice. If you fail to
abide by said vacate notice or if you fail, refuse, or neglect to pay the rent due, I will take
such legal action as the law requires to evict you from the premises, and you will be held
responsible for all rents due under your tenancy.

_____      _____

(Landlord)                               (Date)

_____      _____

(Witness)                                (Date)

_____      _____

(Notary)                                 (Date)

# Transfers and Assignments

# GENERAL BILL OF SALE

FOR VALUE RECEIVED, the undersigned seller hereby sells and transfers unto

_____ (Buyer) and its successors and assigns forever

the following goods and chattels:

Seller warrants and represents that it has good title to said property and full

authority to sell and transfer same and that said goods and chattels are being sold free

and clear of all liens, encumbrances, liabilities and adverse claims.

Seller further warrants that it shall fully defend, protect, indemnify and save

harmless the Buyer and its lawful successors and assigns from all adverse claims.

Seller disclaims any implied warranty of condition, merchantability or fitness for

a particular purpose, said goods being sold in their present condition "as is" and "where

is."

Signed under seal this _____ day of _____ , 19 ___ .

_____
Seller

# WARRANTY BILL OF SALE

Date:

FOR GOOD CONSIDERATION and for the sum of $                              ,

on this date                              , 19   ,                              (Seller)

sells and transfers to                              (Buyer) and its heirs a fee

simple absolute in the following property:

                              (Seller) hereby guarantees that it has good title

to said property and full authority to sell and transfer same and that said property is sold

free of all liens, encumbrances, liabilities and adverse claims of every nature and

description.

                              (Seller) agrees that it will fully defend,

indemnify, protect and save harmless                              (Buyer) and its

heirs from any adverse claim thereto.


_____          _____

(Seller)                                              (Date)

_____          _____

(Buyer)                                              (Date)

_____          _____

(Witness)                                              (Date)

# QUITCLAIM BILL OF SALE

FOR VALUE RECEIVED, the Undersigned (Seller) sells, transfers, assigns and conveys unto                                                        and its successors and assigns with quitclaim covenants only, the following:

Seller hereby sells only such right, title and interest as it may hold; items sold herein are sold subject to such prior liens, encumbrances and adverse claims, if any, that exist.

Signed under seal this                          day of                          , 19        .

_____

# ASSIGNMENT OF ACCOUNTS RECEIVABLE
# WITH RECOURSE

FOR VALUE RECEIVED, the undersigned assigns, sells and transfers all right, title and interest in and to the following account(s) receivable:

The undersigned warrants that said account(s) are legally owing and the undersigned has not received any payment on same.

If any account is not fully paid within                days, said account(s) will be repurchased by the undersigned for the amount then owing on said account(s), the undersigned thereby guaranteeing collection of said receivables.

The undersigned further warrants that it has full title to said receivables and full authority to sell and transfer same and that said receivables are sold free and clear of all liens, encumbrances or any known claims against said accounts.

This agreement shall be binding upon and inure to the benefit of the parties, their successors, assigns, and personal representatives.

Signed under seal this                day of                , 19      .

_____

Witness:

_____

# ASSIGNMENT OF ACCOUNTS RECEIVABLE
## WITH NON-RECOURSE

FOR VALUE RECEIVED, the undersigned assigns, sells and transfers all right, title and interest in and to the following account(s) receivable:

The undersigned warrants that said account(s) are legally owing, and the undersigned has not received any payment on same and has no knowledge of any dispute thereon. Said account(s) are sold without recourse to the undersigned in the event of non-payment.

The undersigned further warrants that it has full title to said receivables and full authority to sell and transfer same and that said receivables are sold free and clear of all liens, encumbrances or any known claims against said account(s).

This agreement shall be binding upon and inure to the benefit of the parties, their successors, assigns, and personal representatives.

Signed under seal this         day of         , 19     .

_____

Witness:

_____

# COPYRIGHT ASSIGNMENT

FOR GOOD CONSIDERATION, the undersigned assigns, sells, and transfers unto _____ and its successors, assigns, personal agents and representatives all right, title and interest in and to the following described copyright:

The undersigned warrants and represents that good title is maintained to said copyright and that it is free of all liens, encumbrances or any known claims against said copyright, including infringement by or against said copyright.

This assignment shall be binding upon and inure to the benefit of the parties, their successors, assigns, personal agents and representatives.

Signed under seal this _____ day of _____, 19___ .

_____

Witness:

_____

# ASSIGNMENT OF INCOME

FOR VALUE RECEIVED, the undersigned assignor hereby irrevocably assigns
and transfers to                                                        all rights to
proceeds, income, rentals, fees, profits or monies that shall be due the undersigned from
                                                                        arising from
the following obligation:


Undersigned warrants that the balance presently owed is $                   and
that there are no known setoffs or defenses to said obligation. Undersigned further
warrants that said contract is without modification and that he has full authority to enter
into this agreement and that the rights assigned hereunder are free and clear of adverse
claims.

This agreement shall be binding upon and inure to the benefit of the parties, and
their successors and assigns.


Signed under seal this                   day of                   , 19      .

_____

Witness:


_____

# ASSIGNMENT OF TRADEMARK

The undersigned                                    (Owner), being the

lawful Owner of a certain trademark registered in the United States Patent Office under

registration number                    dated                         , 19      ,

(Trademark) for good consideration does hereby sell, transfer, assign and convey all

right, title and interest in said Trademark and all rights and goodwill attaching thereto,

unto                                    (Buyer).

Owner warrants that said Trademark is in full force and good standing and there

are no other assignments of rights or licenses granted under said Trademark or known

infringements by or against said Trademark.

Owner further warrants that it is the lawful Owner of said Trademark, that it has

full right and authority to transfer said Trademark and that said Trademark is transferred

free and clear of all liens, encumbrances and adverse claims.

This agreement shall be binding upon and inure to the benefit of the parties, their

successors, assigns and personal representatives.

Signed under seal this                    day of                    , 19      .

By: _____

State of

County of                                                    , 19

Then personally appeared

who acknowledged the foregoing before me.

_____

(Notary Seal)                    Notary Public

# NOTICE OF ASSIGNMENT

Date:

To:

Re:

I refer to a certain debt or obligation due from you to the above captioned party.

On _____ , 19___ , all rights to receive payment on this debt were assigned to the undersigned. A copy of the assignment is attached. We understand the balance owed is $_____ .

Accordingly, please send all future payments on said account to the undersigned at the below address. Checks should be made payable to the undersigned.

It is important that <u>all</u> payments be made as directed to insure credit. You understand this is not a dunning notice nor a reflection on your credit.

We appreciate your cooperation.

Very truly,

_____

_____

Address

_____

# BOND AND/OR STOCK TRANSFER

        FOR VALUE RECEIVED, the Undersigned

of                                          hereby sells, assigns and transfers to

                       of                                     and its

successors and assigns                          stocks/bonds (circle one) of

                       in the principal amount of $                      ,

no(s)                              inclusive, standing in the name of the

undersigned on the books of said company.

        The undersigned hereby irrevocably constitutes and appoints

             as its attorney-in-fact to transfer the said stocks/bonds (circle one) on the

books of said company, with full power of substitution in the premises.


Dated:

 

                                  _____

                                  Signature Guaranteed

                                  _____

                                  Address

                                  _____

# General Legal Forms

# GENERAL CONTRACT

Date:

BE IT KNOWN THAT, this is a binding contract between

(First Party), located at                                    (Address) and

(Second Party), located at                                   (Address)

effective as of                              , 19      .

Pursuant to said contract                                    (First Party)

and                                     (Second Party) agree to the following (describe

agreement):

Sworn to before me

_____        _____

on                        (Date), 19      .      (Notary Public)

My Commission Expires:

# AFFIDAVIT

State of                           )

                                       ss:

County of                        )

BE IT KNOWN that                              (Deponent) is

of legal age and is hereby deposed and being duly sworn, under oath says the following:

_____

(Deponent)

_____

(Date)

Sworn to before me on                        , 19    , (Date) by

                             (Deponent) who acknowledged that the

foregoing statements are true.

_____

(Notary Public)

My Commission Expires:

# GENERAL POWER
# OF ATTORNEY

BE IT ACKNOWLEDGED, that I,

(Name of Principal) hereby appoint and grant a general power of attorney to

(Name of Agent) as my attorney-in-fact, to act in my name as if I were actually present with full power and authority to do and undertake the following:

1.      Sell, buy, trade, lease, mortgage, assign, rent, or dispose of any real or personal property;

2.      Execute, accept, undertake, and perform all contracts in my name;

3.      Deposit, endorse, or withdraw funds to or from any of my bank accounts or safe deposit box;

4.      Borrow, lend, invest or reinvest funds;

5.      Initiate, defend, commence or settle legal actions on my behalf;

6.      Vote (in person or by proxy) any shares or beneficial interest in any entity;

7.      Retain any accountant, attorney or other advisor deemed necessary to protect my interests relative to any of the foregoing.

This power of attorney may be revoked by

(Principal) at any time but shall not be affected by

(Principal's) subsequent disability or incompetence. This power of attorney shall automatically be revoked upon death of

(Principal) provided any person relying on this power of attorney shall have full rights to accept the authority of my attorney-in-fact until actual notice of revocation is received.

---

(Principal)

---

(Date)


State of                                  )
                                                  ss:

County of                                )


Sworn to before me by                                (Principal) on

                    , 19     (Date).

---

Notary Public

My Commission Expires:

# REVOCATION OF
# POWER OF ATTORNEY


BE IT KNOWN THAT,                    (Principal)

hereby revokes, countermands, annuls, and voids said Power of Attorney appointed and

granted to                    (Name of Agent) on

       (Date) for the following reasons:


_____

(Signature of Principal)        (Date)


Sworn to before me by                  (Principal) on

       , 19     (Date).


_____

Notary Public

My Commission Expires:

# INDIVIDUAL
# ACKNOWLEDGEMENT

State of

County of


     On this                 day of                    , 19    ,

before me personally appeared                          , known

by me to be the individual described in and who executed the document annexed hereto

and who executed same in my presence or acknowledged said signature as a true and

free act and deed.


                                    _____

                                    Notary Public

                                    My Commission Expires:

# CORPORATE
# ACKNOWLEDGEMENT


State of

County of


On this                              day of                                    , 19     , before

me personally appeared                                                    , who, duly

sworn, did depose and say that he is the                                        of

                                        , the corporation described in and which

executed the annexed document; that he knows the seal of said corporation; that the seal

affixed is such corporate seal; that it was so affixed by order of the Board of Directors of

said corporation; and that he signed his name thereto by like order.


_____

Notary Public

My Commission Expires:

# RECEIPT IN FULL

The undersigned hereby acknowledges receipt of the sum of $

paid by                                                    . This payment constitutes full

discharge and satisfaction of the following obligation.




Signed under seal this                    day of                    , 19        .

                                        _____

# RECEIPT ON ACCOUNT

Date:

I hereby acknowledge receipt of the sum of $        from
this date by cash _____ check _____ to be applied and
credited to the below described account:

_____

# SIGHT DRAFT

Date:

To: (Bank)

Upon due presentment, you shall pay to the order of

the sum of                    ($              ) Dollars and debit my account for said

amount.

_____

Account Name

By: _____

Authorized Signature

_____

Account Number

# NOTICE OF
# DISHONORED CHECK

Date:

To:

      Your check no.               in the amount of $             dated
, 19   , has been dishonored by your bank. We have verified
with your bank that there are still insufficient funds to pay the check.

      Demand is made upon you to replace this check with cash (or certified check)
within            days (or such further time as may be allowed pursuant to state
law), or we shall take immediate legal action.

            Sincerely,

_____

# STOP-PAYMENT ORDER

Date:

To: (Bank)

Please refuse payment upon presentment of the following check:

Name of Payee

Date of Check

Check Number

Amount

This stop payment order remains in effect until further written notice.

Please advise if you have previously paid this check.

_____

Name of Account

_____

Account Number

By: _____

_____

Title

Re-issue after six months

# STOP-PAYMENT
# ORDER CANCELLATION

Date:

To:  (Bank)


On                              , 19      , we requested that you stop payment on
the below check:

Check No:

Dated:

Amount:

Maker:

Payee:

Account No:

We cancel this stop-payment order; you may now pay this check.


_____

Name of Account

_____

Account Number


By: _____

# BULK SALES NOTICE

Date:

Notice to Creditors of:

Please note that                                              (Seller/Transferor)

under Article 6 of the Uniform Commercial Code, shall make a bulk sale and transfer all

or substantially all its goods on                    (Date) to

           (Buyer/Transferee) located at the following premises:

(Address of Buyer)

       To the knowledge of Buyer, Seller has not conducted its business under any

other name or address during the preceding three years. As a result of said bulk sale

transaction, all debts of Seller shall be paid in full as they fall due pursuant this bulk sale.

       Creditors shall forward bills and invoices to                    (Buyer)

at the following address                              no later than

           (Date).

_____        _____

(Buyer)                                (Date)

# COVENANT NOT TO SUE

FOR GOOD CONSIDERATION RECEIVED, the Undersigned, being the

holder of an actual, asserted or prospective claim against

arising from:

do hereby covenant that I/we shall not commence nor maintain any suit thereon against

said party whether in law or in equity provided nothing herein shall constitute a release.

This covenant shall be binding upon and inure to the benefit of the parties, their

successors, assigns and executors, administrators, personal representatives and heirs.

The Undersigned affixes and signs under seal this       day of

, 19    .

_____     _____

State of

County of                                       , 19

Subscribed and sworn to before me on this       day of

, 19   .

_____

Notary Public

My Commission Expires:

# RELEASE OF MECHANICS' LIENS

FOR VALUABLE CONSIDERATION, the undersigned contractors or sub-contractors having furnished materials and/or labor for construction at the premises known as                                                            ,
owned by                                                        , do hereby release all liens or rights to file liens against said property for material and/or services or labor provided to this date, with it acknowledged, however, that this discharge shall     shall not        necessarily constitute a release or discharge of any sums now or hereinafter due for said material and/or services.

This release shall be binding upon and inure to the benefit of the parties, their successors, assigns and personal representatives.

Signed under seal this                         day of                    , 19     .

Witnessed:

_____     By: _____
                                                           Contractor/Subcontractor

# PERMISSION REQUEST

Date:


Name of Requester:

Copyright Holder:


      BE IT KNOWN THAT,                        (Copyright

Holder) hereby grants permission to                 (Name of

Requester) to use, reproduce, reprint and publish said material described below for

distribution in (circle all that apply):

1.      The United States

2.      Canada

3.      Europe

4.      South America

5.      Canada

6.      World


      Material granted to be used, reproduced, reprinted, and published includes the

following:

Author:

Title:

Selection:

Date of Copyright:

Limitations/Conditions to said grant of permission by                    (Copyright Holder)

to                          (Requester) include:

_____          _____

(Copyright Holder)                                    (Date)


_____          _____

(Requester)                                              (Date)

# PERMISSION TO USE QUOTE
# OR PERSONAL STATEMENT

FOR VALUABLE CONSIDERATION, the undersigned irrevocably grants to _____ and its successors and assigns the world-wide rights to use, publish or reprint in whole or in part the following statement, picture, endorsement or quotation:

This agreement shall be binding upon and inure to the benefit of the parties, their successors, assigns and personal representatives.

Signed under seal this _____ day of _____, 19____.

Witnessed:

_____     _____

# PURCHASE OPTION

AGREEMENT between

(Owner) and                                        (Buyer). For valuable

consideration, it is agreed that:

1.      Buyer hereby pays to Owner the sum of $                    in

consideration for this option, which option payment shall          shall not

be credited to the purchase price if the option is exercised.

2.      Buyer has the option and right to buy


(property) during the option period for the full purchase price of $                    .

3.      This option shall remain in effect until                    , 19      , and

then expire.

4.      To exercise this option, Buyer shall notify Owner of same by certified mail,

return receipt, within the option period.

5.      Upon exercise of this option, the Owner and Buyer agree to sign the attached

and completed contract of sale and to consummate the sale on its terms.

6.      This option agreement shall be binding upon and inure to the benefit of the

parties, their successors, assigns and personal representatives.

Signed under seal this                    day of                    , 19      .


Witnessed:


_____          _____


_____          _____

# GIFT ACKNOWLEDGEMENT

I/we                                                    hereby make a

non-revocable gift of the following:

to:                                                    and his or her successors and

assigns, forever.

This gift shall not be considered an advance towards any testamentary gift or

bequest I may make to the aforesaid                    .

Signed under seal this          day of          , 19    .

_____

# NAME REMOVAL REQUEST

Date:

To:

Direct Mail Firm

I receive unsolicited mail from your firm and would appreciate your removing my name from your mailing list.

_____
Name

_____
Address

_____
City, State, Zip

Thank you for your prompt attention.

Sincerely,

_____

# NOTICE OF DISPUTED
# ACCOUNT BALANCE

Date:

To:

We have your invoice or statement no.                    , dated                    ,

19      , for $                    .

We dispute this for the following reason(s):

_____ We have not received the items billed.

_____ Your prices are above the agreed amount.

_____ We paid $                    on                                        ,

19        , and it has not been credited.

_____ Goods were not ordered.

_____ Goods were defective (specify)

_____ Goods are available for return as per your return/credit policy.

_____ Other: (Describe)

See reverse side for any additional information or explanation.

Sincerely,

_____

# PAYMENT ON SPECIFIC ACCOUNTS

Date:

To:

      Our enclosed check no.            for $          should be credited to the following charges or invoices only:

| Invoice/Debt | Amount |
| --- | --- |
| | $ |
| | $ |
| | $ |
| | $ |
| | $ |

      Payments herein shall be applied only to those specified items listed and shall not be applied, in whole or in part, to other obligations.

Sincerely,

_____

## CIVIL SERVICE BOOKS

### TEST PREPARATION

Accountant / Auditor
ACWA: Administrative Careers With America
Air Traffic Controller Qualifying Test
Air Traffic Controller Training Program
American Foreign Service Officer
Beginning Clerical Worker
Bookkeeper / Account Clerk
Building Custodian / Building Superintendent /
    Custodian Engineer
Bus Operator / Conductor
Case Worker
Computer Specialist GS 5-9
The Corey Guide to Postal Exams
Correction Officer
Correction Officer Promotion Tests
Court Officer / Senior Court Officer / Court Clerk
Distribution Clerk, Machine
Drug Enforcement Agent
Electrician / Electrician's Helper
Emergency Dispatcher / 911 Operator
Federal Clerk / Steno / Typist
File Clerk / General Clerk
Fire Department Lieutenant / Captain /
    Battalion Chief
Firefighter
Gardener / Grounds Maintenance Worker
Investigator / Claim Examiner
Law Enforcement Exams Handbook
Machinist / Machinist's Helper
Mail Handler / Mail Processor
Maintenance Worker / Mechanical Maintainer
Mark-up Clerk / Clerk Typist /
    Clerk Stenographer—U.S. Postal Service
Plumber / Steam Fitter
Police Administrative Aide
Police Officer
Police Sergeant / Lieutenant / Captain

Postal Exams Handbook
Post Office Clerk / Carrier
Preparación para el examen de cartero
Probation Officer / Parole Officer
Rural Carrier
Sanitation Worker
Senior Clerical Series
Special Agent
Special Officer / Senior Special Officer /
    Bridge and Tunnel Officer
State Trooper / Highway Patrol Officer /
    State Traffic Officer
Track Worker
Traffic Enforcement Agent
Train Operator / Tower Operator / Assistant
    Train Dispatcher

### CAREERS / STUDY GUIDES

Civil Service Administrative Tests
Civil Service Arithmetic and Vocabulary
Civil Service Clerical Promotion Tests
Civil Service Handbook
Civil Service Psychological and Psychiatric
    Tests
Civil Service Reading Comprehension Tests
Civil Service Tests for Basic Skills Jobs
Complete Guide to U.S. Civil Service Jobs
Federal Jobs for College Graduates
Federal Jobs in Law Enforcement
General Test Practice for 101 U.S. Jobs
How to Get a Clerical Job in Government
Practice for Clerical, Typing and
    Stenographic Tests
SF 171: The Federal Employment
    Application Form
Supervision

**AVAILABLE AT BOOKSTORES EVERYWHERE**